DATE DUE

MAR 3 1 1987			

Goodheart-Willcox's BUILD-A-COURSE Series

LEATHERCRAFT

by

FRED W. ZIMMERMAN

Professor of Industrial Arts
Western Illinois University, Macomb

WALTER C. BROWN, Consulting Editor
Supervisor of Industrial Arts
Director of Vocational-Technical Education
Phoenix, Arizona

Books in Build-A-Course Series

Woodworking—Wagner

Drafting—Brown

Electricity—Gerrish

Electronics—Gerrish

Metalworking—Boyd

Art Metals—Siegner

Graphics Arts—Kagy

Power Mechanics—Atteberry

Leathercraft—Zimmerman

Ceramics—Brennan

Plastics—Cope

(Other books in work)

South Holland, Ill.
THE GOODHEART-WILLCOX CO., Inc.
Publishers

INTRODUCTION

This book on LEATHERCRAFT will acquaint you with the Tools, Terms, and Procedures of Carving and Stamping Leather.

Pictorial step-by-step procedures will guide you to completion of useful and attractive projects. By comparing each step of your work with the work shown in the photos, surprising results may be obtained.

LEATHERCRAFT will help you develop SAFE work habits; it will assist you in designing and creating your own projects.

The book provides, too, information on the importance of Leather in our everyday lives.

In exploring the industrial areas, you may find that the work interests you to the extent you will want to pursue it as your future livelihood. Or, you may find it is of more interest as a hobby. In either case, a knowledge of LEATHERCRAFT will be a worthwhile part of your general education.

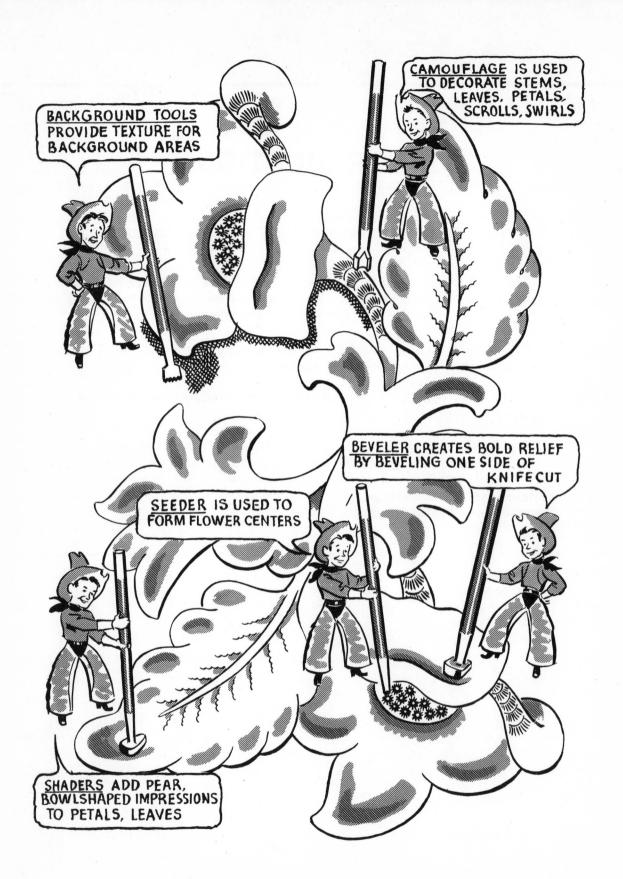

These "doodles" by artist Carl Pemble illustrate uses
of stamping tools in decorating leather projects.

CONTENTS

STARTING IN LEATHERCRAFT

UNIT 1

1. Introduction
2. Project analysis
3. Leather classification, uses
4. Tool identification
5. First Project

A CHAT WITH YOUR TEACHER

In working with leather we need not follow a set pattern of experiences, but rather employ ingenuity, inventiveness and creativeness in doing all of our projects.

Figure 1-1 lists the processes or procedures involved in the making of the projects presented in this book. The projects are arranged in groups beginning with simple projects requiring only a few processes, and proceeding toward more difficult projects requiring more time and effort. A variety of projects is presented in all groups so that you may choose to meet your interests and skill. Newly created projects may be added to any group.

The analysis chart, Fig. 1-1, is prepared to:

1. Serve you as a means of direction and guidance. For example, you may wish to make a project of your own creation that involves processes of two or more groups. From the chart you can quickly determine which projects involve processes in which you are particularly interested.
2. Serve you as an instrument or guide for learning various processes or procedures.
3. Help you to learn an orderly method

of procedure in planning and constructing projects.
4. Encourage you to carefully analyze the processes involved in project development.
5. Discourage you from attempting projects which are too difficult.
6. Encourage you to create your own projects.
7. Create a systematic method of organizing industrial arts projects, which may be used for other Industrial Arts areas.

BOOK ARRANGEMENT

The material in this book is arranged in units. Each unit contains an information lesson and a group of projects. The groups of projects are arranged so you may begin with the less difficult, and proceed toward projects involving more complicated designs and procedures.

Study closely the information section of each unit. The knowledge you gain will help you to be successful with the projects which follow.

LEATHER AND YOU

Leather is one of the most useful products of our modern industry. Most of the shoes we wear and many of our gloves and garments are made of leather. Billfolds, handbags, and other fancy goods

PROCESSES	UNIT 1	UNIT 2							UNIT 3					UNIT 4					
	Post Key Case	Pencil Case	Comb Case	Book Mark	Coaster	Paper Weight	Blotter Corner	Glasses Case	Coin Purse	Picture & Card Holder	Cigarette Case	Nail File & Comb Case	Memo Pad	Billfold	Frame Key Case	Knife Case	Belt	Book End	Letter Holder
Making Templates	X	X	X	X	X	X	X	X	X	X	X	X	X	X	X	X	X	X	X
Transferring Templates to Leather	X	X	X	X	X	X	X	X	X	X	X	X	X	X	X	X	X	X	X
Conditioning Leather	X	X	X	X	X	X	X	X	X	X	X	X	X	X	X	X	X	X	X
Applying Finish	X	X	X	X	X	X	X	X	X	X	X	X	X	X	X	X	X	X	X
Preparing Designs		X	X	X	X	X	X	X	X	X	X	X	X	X	X	X	X	X	X
Transferring Designs to Leather		X	X	X	X	X	X	X	X	X	X	X	X	X	X	X	X	X	X
Modeling		X	X	X	X	X	X	X	X	X	X	X	X	X	X	X	X	X	X
Skiving Edges		X	X			X	X	X	X	X	X	X	X	X	X	X	X	X	X
Cementing		X	X			X	X	X	X	X	X	X	X	X	X	X	X	X	X
Assembling Leather Parts		X	X			X	X	X	X	X	X	X	X	X	X	X	X	X	X
Thonging		X	X			X	X	X	X	X	X	X	X	X	X	X	X	X	X
Cutting with Skiving Knife		X	X	X			X	X	X	X	X	X	X	X	X	X	X	X	X
Cutting with Scissors	X	X	X		X	X		X	X	X	X			X	X	X	X	X	X
Edge Beveling	X			X	X		X	X	X	X	X	X	X	X	X	X	X	X	X
Edge Creasing	X			X	X		X	X	X	X	X	X	X	X	X	X	X	X	X
Incising with Carving Knife									X	X	X	X	X	X	X	X	X	X	X
Lacing with Double Buttonhole Stitch									X	X	X	X	X	X	X	X		X	X
Embossing									X	X	X	X	X	X	X	X			
Making Background with Tracing Tool		X	X	X	X	X	X	X											
Attaching Skiver Lining									X	X	X	X	X	X	X				
Trimming Skiver Lining									X	X	X	X	X	X	X				
Attaching Snap Button	X	X							X		X				X	X	X		
Cutting Groove to Make Fold									X	X	X	X	X	X	X				
Camouflaging														X	X	X	X	X	X
Shading														X	X	X	X	X	X
Beveling														X	X	X	X	X	X
Forming Background with Stamping Tools														X	X	X	X	X	X
Veining														X	X	X	X	X	X
Seeding														X	X	X	X	X	X
Using Mulefoot Tool														X	X	X	X	X	X
Make Decorative Cut														X	X	X	X	X	X
Dyeing Background														X	X	X	X	X	X
Lacing with Whip Stitch		X	X			X	X	X											
Forming Background with Deer's Foot Tool									X	X	X	X	X						
Spacing Stitches														X	X	X	X		
Punching Holes for Stitching with Awl														X	X	X	X		
Stitching with Thread														X	X	X	X		
Setting Eyelets															X	X			
Setting Rivets															X	X			
Metal Layout																		X	X
Cutting Metal																		X	X
Bending Metal																		X	X
Assembling Post	X																		
Number of Processes in Project	9	16	15	11	11	14	16	17	23	22	23	21	21	33	36	33	29	29	29

Fig. 1-1. Processes involved in making projects described in this book.

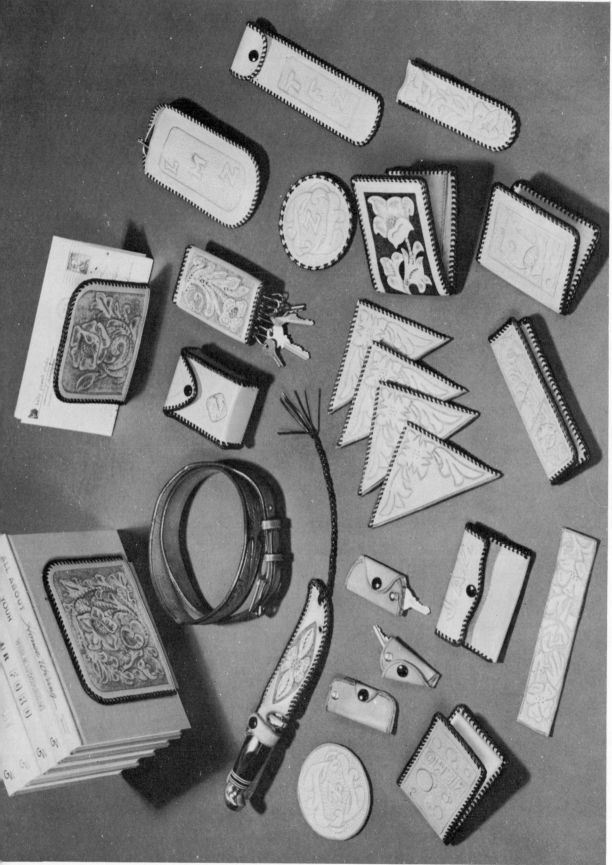

Fig. 1-2. Leathercraft project suggestions.

made of leather are common throughout our great country.

The tremendous industrial growth of our country has created jobs of many kinds and descriptions. You may soon be preparing yourself for one of these jobs. It is most important that you select your occupation wisely so you will be productive and happy in your work.

While doing work in leathercraft, you will become acquainted with many of the tools, materials, processes, and products essential in this work. You will gain experience in orderly procedures of doing jobs. Be sure to take advantage of the ideas and experiences of your fellow students and help them whenever you can. Help yourself and your teacher by completing each lesson and project with a maximum of care.

PROJECT SELECTION

The projects illustrated in Fig. 1-2 are only a few ideas for useful items that can be made in this area. Maybe they will give you ideas which will help you create projects of your own design. Use your imagination freely.

In starting out it is advisable to select your first projects from Unit 1 or Unit 2 projects. This will enable you to acquire skill on inexpensive projects. The experience you gain will enable you to enjoy success with your more advanced projects.

LEATHER SOURCES

Leather is a pliable and durable material made from animal pelts. Animal pelts comprise about 7 per cent of the animal weight and are by-products of other industries. An animal pelt freshly removed from an animal carcass contains about 70 per cent water. When the pelt is chemically treated with certain materials in a process called tanning, it becomes resist-

ant to bacteria and water and is called "leather." A pelt left untreated is immediately attacked by bacteria and enzymes causing it to deteriorate. A pelt if allowed to dry out, becomes hard and brittle and is of no commercial value.

ANCIENT USES OF LEATHER

Man's use of leather began many centuries ago. The ancient pyramids of the Egyptians have revealed that leather was in use hundreds of years before the birth of Christ. Modern excavations in Egypt have unearthed articles believed to be over 33 centuries old which are still in good condition. Leather was prized like gold, silver, rare woods, and other valued treasurers by the early Egyptians and their neighbors. The Romans once employed it as a basis for money. The ancient Greeks used leather for armor, ship sails, even housing and clothes.

EARLY EUROPEAN USES OF LEATHER

In Europe before the discovery of America, leather was produced in sizable amounts. The leather industry developed skilled workmen in England and France who formed trade guilds. These were among the first workmen's associations and were the forerunners of our modern industrial unions.

EARLY AMERICAN USES OF LEATHER

The early settlers in our own country found some of the Indians to be highly skilled in the art of leatherworking. They used leather for clothing, footwear, bedding, shelter and many other purposes. Methods of tanning varied with different tribes. The Navahos and Crows are believed to have been the most highly skilled in the art. The Navahos were especially noted for their decorations of leather, while the Crows were more adept in tanning leather. The process which they had perfected for dressing a soft type of leather known as "buckskin tan," which they taught to the early settlers, is basically the one we use today. For softness, water resistance, and flexibility it is unexcelled.

MODERN USES OF LEATHER

Over three-fourths of all the leather consumed in our country goes for the production of shoes. A large part of the remainder is used for making fancy leather goods, · handbags, gloves and garments, upholstery, and for bookbinding. The production of leather products is one of the most important industries of our country.

WEIGHTS OF LEATHER

Leather supply companies indicate thicknesses of leather by using the term OUNCES (oz.). An ounce is considered to be leather 1/64 in. in thickness. Since thickness and weights of leather tend to vary slightly, double weights are usually given. For example, 2/3 oz. meaning 2/64 to 3/64 inch in thickness or 7/8 oz. meaning 7/64 to 8/64 inch in thickness, etc. Leather is sold by the square foot, pound or skin. Alligator, lizard and snake skins are sometimes sold by the inch measurement across the widest part.

CLASSIFICATION OF LEATHER

The leather produced from small animals such as calves, sheep and goats is usually referred to as SKINS. A full calfskin usually runs 9 to 15 square feet, Fig. 1-3.

Leather made from the pelts of large animals such as cows, is usually referred to as HIDES. A side is one-half of a full hide and usually runs 22 to 26 square feet for cowhide, Fig. 1-4. A KIP is one-half of a heavy calfskin (sometimes referred to as senior calfskin) and runs about 9 to 17 square feet. A BELLY is the lower portion of a side. It has more waste

Fig. 1-3. Full skin or full hide.

so is usually cheaper per square foot, Fig. 1-4. BACKS are usually considered the best leather by leathercrafters. Backs have less waste and usually cost more per square foot.

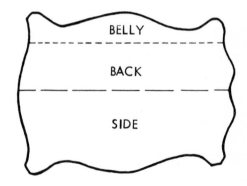

Fig. 1-4. Parts of a full skin.

LEATHERWORKING TOOLS

Descriptions of tools commonly used in leathercraft work and shown in Fig. 1-5 follow:

1. PENCIL, for preparing patterns and designs.
2. SKIFE, for skiving or trimming leather edges to be joined. You can use

this tool as a substitute for a skiving knife. It is made to take certain types of razor blades as cutting edges. Razor blades can be inserted or removed which eliminates necessity of sharpening this tool.

3. SKIVING KNIFE, for cutting leather and for thinning edges of leather. Lacing materials will cover thinned edges more easily than bulky edges.

4. SHEARS, to cut leather. This is a sturdy tool which we can use to cut thick, medium, or thin leather. You can substitute ordinary household scissors

for shears to cut thin and medium leathers.

5. SQUARE, for laying out projects and measuring leather.

6. SPOON AND TRACER MODELING TOOL, for tracing designs on leather and for compressing leather.

7. TRACING TOOL, for tracing designs on leather.

8. WOOD MALLET, to attach snap buttons and rivets, and for stamping backgrounds.

9. BALL MODELING TOOL, for compressing small areas of leather not easily

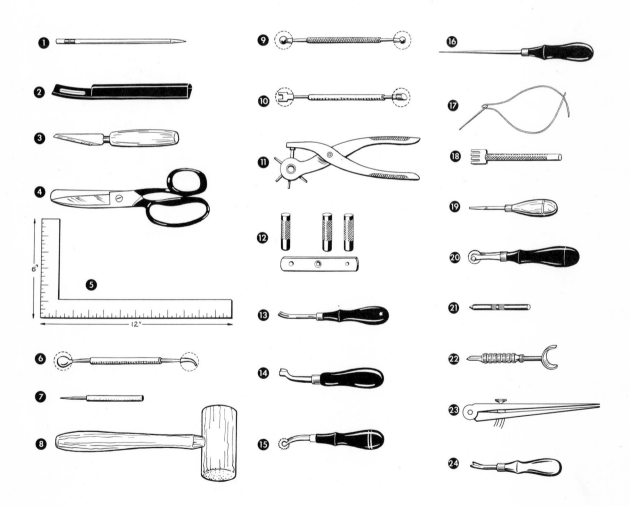

Fig. 1-5. Leather-working tools. 1-Pencil, 2-Skife, 3-Skiving knife, 4-Shears, 5-Square, 6-Spoon and tracer modeling tool, 7-Tracing tool, 8 Wood mallet, 9-Ball modeling tool, 10-Deer's foot and double line marking tool, 11-Revolving spring punch, 12-Snap button set, 13-Edge beveler, 14-Edge creaser, 15-Spacing wheel, 16-Awl, 17-Harness needle, 18-Thonging chisel, 19-Fid, 29-Embossing wheel, 21-Eyelet setter, 22-Swivel carving knife, 23-Dividers, 24-Gouge.

accessible with other modeling tools.

10.   DEER'S FOOT AND DOUBLE LINE MARKING TOOL, for backgrounds and for marking a line as a guide to lacing.

11.   REVOLVING SPRING PUNCH, for punching holes through leather. This punch has six punching cylinders of variable sizes. The #1 cylinder punches the smallest hole, #6 the largest.

12.   SNAP BUTTON SET, for attaching segma and bird-cage snap buttons.

13.   EDGE BEVELER, to cut away a portion of the edges of leather in preparation for your use of the edge creaser.

14.   EDGE CREASER, to round edges of leather not to be laced. A small groove is made at variable distances from the edge of the leather depending upon the size of the edge creaser you use. The #1 edge creaser is the smallest size.

15.   SPACING WHEEL, for marking equidistant spaces on leather before punching holes for sewing.

16.   AWL, for punching small holes through leather at the points marked by spacing wheel. A small board should be used under the leather to prevent marring your bench.

17.   HARNESS NEEDLE, for stitching pieces of leather together where lacing is less satisfactory.

18.   THONGING CHISEL, for punching slits through leather in preparation for lacing.   This tool is available with one punching prong and with multiple punching prongs.   A four-prong chisel is shown.   You can purchase both 3/32 in. width and 1/8 in. width prongs.

19.   FID, for opening thong slits.   A tracing tool or nut pick may be used as a substitute.

20.   EMBOSSING WHEEL, to produce a continuous decorative design along edges of leather not to be laced.   You can use the embossing wheel frequently on inside pockets of coin purses, frame key cases, and billfolds.

21.   EYELET SETTER, for setting eyelets.   This tool has a taper at one end which is to be inserted into the eyelet and tapped with a small mallet.   The light tapping flares the eyelet, holding it in place.

22.   SWIVEL CARVING KNIFE, for incising or part way cutting through the leather.   You can produce deep tooling and stamping of designs by using this tool.

23.   DIVIDERS, to scribe and divide lines, gauge uniformity.

24.   GOUGE, to cut grooves in leather. Leather is grooved so it will fold properly.

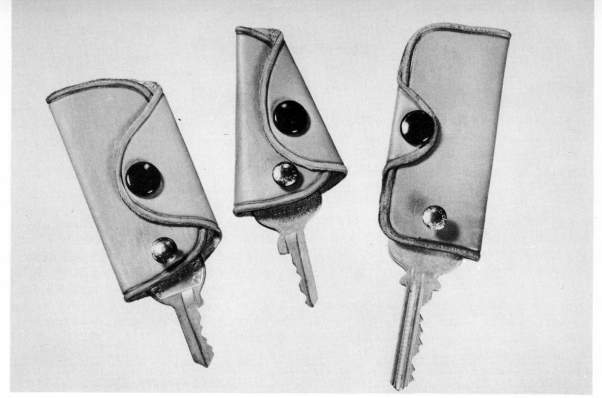

Fig. 1-6. Three styles of post key cases.

POST KEY CASES

The projects suggested in this unit are post key cases of several designs. A post key case is designed to hold four or five keys, and being small, is easily carried. A post key case (Fig. 1-6) is something that can be used by almost everyone.

TOOLS REQUIRED

In making Unit 1 Projects you will need: pencil, scissors, edge beveler, small sponge or rag, edge creaser, snap button set.

MATERIAL REQUIRED

Tooling Cowhide

Lightweight tooling cowhide (approximately 3/4 oz.), is highly desirable for small projects, especially where durability is important, as in key cases. You can make the projects of Unit 1 with small pieces of leather which are left over from larger projects. If small pieces are not available, it is advisable to use the leather next to the edge of the skin.

Accessories

Snap Button. -- A segma snap button consists of four parts: a cap, a cap socket, a stud, and an eyelet, Fig. 1-7 The parts

BUTTON   SOCKET   STUD   EYELET

Fig. 1-7. Parts of a segma snap button.

may be fastened to leather with a snap button set. You will use snap buttons to hold closed such projects as key cases and coin purses.

Binder post. -- A binder post consists of two parts: a post and a cap. The two parts are screwed together to form a binder post, useful to hold keys or pictures (see Fig. 1-22, p. 19).

Finishes

Diluted oxalic acid.--This is a bleaching material which removes dirt and finger prints from leather. A clean leather surface is desirable before you apply a finish. Oxalic acid comes in powder form and should be diluted (one part oxalic acid to about 20 parts of water). You can apply it to leather surfaces with a small cloth. Rinsing is not necessary unless you use a stronger solution.

Leather dressing and finisher--This material contains essential oils and waxes which seal the pores of leather and leave a lustre finish on the surface. It protects leather from soiling and dampness. Special preparations are sold by most leather supply houses.

Wax--Wax is used as a protective coating on the surfaces of leather. It gives leather a hard water-resistant coating, and will buff to a high gloss. There are many liquid and paste waxes available at local grocery and department stores. Even ordinary wax shoe polish may be used. You may apply wax over leather dressing or directly onto the grain surface of the leather.

SAMMY SAFETY
Says:

"You are now forming habits that you may keep all of your life. Let's make them good habits. We can work more easily and effectively if we work safely. Your contribution is most important to safe and efficient operation of our program.

1. Let's learn to work together. Can you imagine how many different workers are needed to make the swivel knife? Cooperation is necessary in every phase of our industrial life. Always do your part.
2. Be courteous and helpful to others. Consider the safety of your classmates and always treat them as you would like to be treated.
3. Ask your instructor to approve your plan before you begin work on a project.
4. Caution any classmate you see who is violating a safety rule.
5. Keep your bench and cabinet lockers closed.
6. Handle carefully any glass bottles or jars.
7. Wipe up immediately any spilled liquid materials.
8. Place oily rags and other combustible materials in the metal container provided.
9. Report any injury, no matter how slight, to your instructor."

About Handling Tools,

SAMMY SAYS:

"1. Our tools are our friends. Care for tools as if you earned the money to buy them.

2. Handle edge and pointed tools with care. Keep them out of your pockets.
3. Be sure your hands are free of dirt and grease before you begin work.
4. Always pass tools to your classmates with the handles first.
5. Use only tools that are sharp and in good condition.
6. Use the correct kind of tool to do the job at hand. Check with your instructor if you are in doubt."

For a Clean and Orderly Shop,

SAMMY SAYS:

"A good housekeeper is a safe, efficient worker. We must keep our shop neat and clean to receive maximum benefit through its use.

1. Keep the area clean in which you work.
2. Check out only the materials necessary for your project.
3. Return all tools and unused materials to their proper places.
4. Report any broken or missing tools.
5. Cooperate with your classmates in the student management program."

About Handling Oxalic Acid,

SAMMY SAYS:

"1. Keep oxalic acid solution away from your eyes.
2. Wash any affected area of your skin or eyes with clean water. Apply a solution of baking soda and water to your skin to neutralize the acid."

PROCEDURE FOR MAKING POST KEY CASES

1.   Make a template.
 a.   Choose one of the full-size patterns
      (Figs. 1-8, 1-9, 1-10), or use your
      own design.   Make a template of

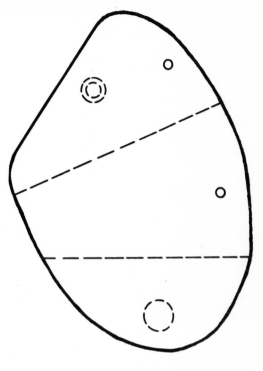

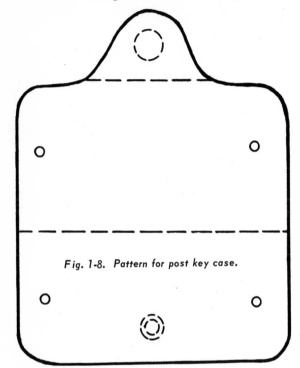

Fig. 1-8. *Pattern for post key case.*

Fig. 1-10. *Another alternate design for post key case.*

cardboard, pressed wood, or metal.

 b.   You can make a template by follow-
      ing this procedure.
  (1)   Place a piece of tracing paper
        over the drawing you select and
        trace the design on the paper,
        using a pencil.
  (2)   Cement the tracing paper to a
        piece of cardboard, pressed wood
        or metal.
  (3)   Cut out the template, carefully
        following the lines.
  (4)   Apply a coat of clear lacquer,
        shellac, or varnish to the sur-
        face of the template to make it
        durable.
2.   Transfer the template to leather.
     Trace around the template onto tool-
     ing cowhide with an ordinary lead
     pencil, Fig. 1-11
3.   Cut with scissors.
     Cut out the leather with scissors or

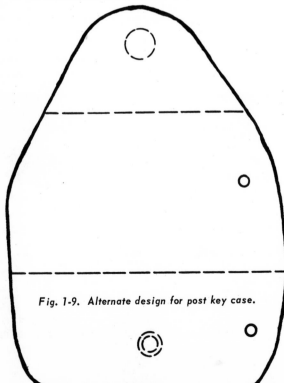

Fig. 1-9. *Alternate design for post key case.*

a sharp knife. Fig. 1-12. You can easily use ordinary household scissors when cutting leather up to 3-1/2 oz. or 1/16 in. thickness. You should use shears to cut leather which is thicker than 1/16 in.

4. Bevel the edges.

Thin the edges from the grain side of the leather with an edge beveler.

Fig. 1-11. Transferring template to leather.

Fig. 1-12. Cutting around template with scissors.

This tool has a U or V-shaped cutting knife and cuts with a forward stroke. Fig. 1-13 .

5. Condition edges to be creased.

Dampen the flesh side (rough side) of the leather with a sponge or cloth

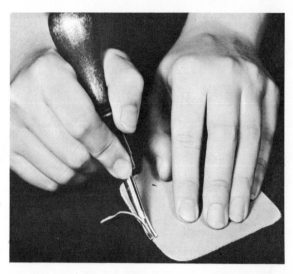

Fig. 1-13. Using edge beveler to bevel edges.

(Fig. 1-14). Correct moisture content causes leather to respond well to pressure of tools. The entire piece should be moistened to help prevent water spots. Leather will absorb moisture more readily if applied to the flesh side. You must take care to prevent excessive moisture. A good rule is to keep

Fig. 1-14. Conditioning leather.

applying moisture in small quantities until the leather responds well

to modeling tools. Too much moisture will result in spongy leather which will not hold tool marks. Too little water will cause stiff leather which is difficult to tool. Experimenting on a piece of scrap leather is desirable. If tooling requires more than one class period, place your project in a plastic bag to keep

a #2 hole where you made the pencil mark.

Fig. 1-16. Punching a #6 hole.

Fig. 1-15. Creasing the edges.

d. Assemble the cap and cap socket, Fig. 1-18 and 1-20.
   (1) Place the cap socket through the #6 hole from the flesh side of the leather and place the cap on top.
   (2) Proceed with a snap button set and small mallet.

it moist until you get back to the job. Place the plastic bag in a cool place to prevent possible molding.

6. Crease edges with an edge creaser. An edge creaser rounds the edges and makes a uniform line near the edge, depending upon the size of tool you use, Fig. 1-15.
7. Attach a snap button.
a. Punch a #6 hole with a revolving spring punch in the flap of your key case, to receive the cap and cap socket. The #6 punching cylinder is the largest cylinder on a revolving spring punch. See Figs. 1-16 and 1-20.
b. Fold your key case into its permanent position and mark through the #6 hole you previously punched, as shown in Fig. 1-17.
c. Unfold your key case and punch

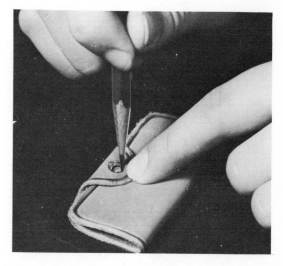

Fig. 1-17. Marking through the #6 hole.

e. Assemble the eyelet and stud, Figs. 1-19 and 1-20.
   (1) Place the eyelet through the #3 hole from the flesh side

of the leather and place the stud over it.

(2) Proceed with a snap button set and small mallet.

8. Apply a finish, Fig. 1-21.

a. Apply a coat of diluted oxalic acid solution with a small cloth. Allow

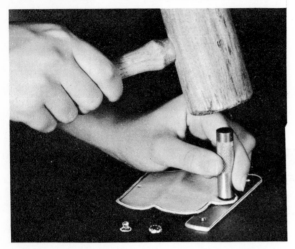

Fig. 1-18. Assembling the cap and cap socket.

your project to dry. This usually takes about twelve hours.

b. Apply one or more coats of leather

dressing with a small cloth or sponge. Allow the leather dressing to dry thoroughly.

c. Apply one or more coats of a neutral shade paste shoe wax. Wait

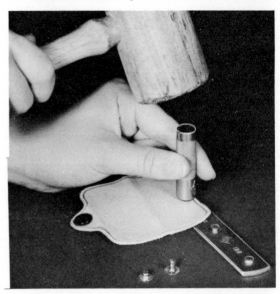

Fig. 1-19. Assembling the eyelet and stud.

a few minutes, then polish your project with a soft cloth.

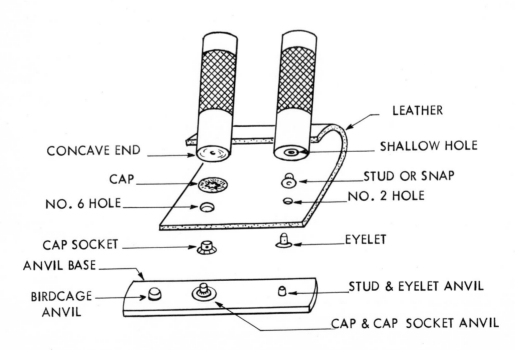

Fig. 1-20. Snap button assembly.

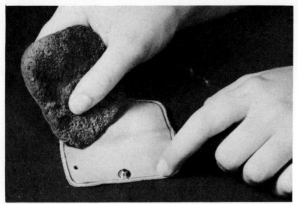

Fig. 1-21. Applying finish.

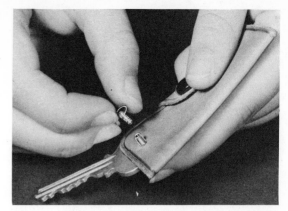

Fig. 1-22. Assembling the post.

9. Assemble the post.
The post is made of two threaded parts. Punch a #2 hole with a revolving spring punch. Insert one part through the #2 hole, and screw the other part into it, Fig. 1-22.

QUIZ - Unit 1

Write your answers on a separate sheet of paper. Do NOT write in this book.

1. A pelt freshly removed from an animal carcass contains about_____per cent water.
2. When we speak of leather being tanned, what do we mean?
3. For what purposes did the American Indians use leather?
4. Weights of leather are indicated by using the term ounces (oz.). An ounce is leather with a thickness of 1/64 in., 1/32 in., 3/64 in., or 1/8 in.
5. The lower portion of a side of leather is called_____
6. Leather made from the pelt of a large animal such as a cow is referred to as a hide, kip, skin, or side?
7. Which is considered the better leather, the back or the belly? Why?
8. One half of a heavy calfskin is usually called a_____.
9. One half of a full cowhide is called a_____.
10. What do we mean by the term "skin?"
11. Identify and describe briefly the purpose for which these tools are used:

A B C D E F

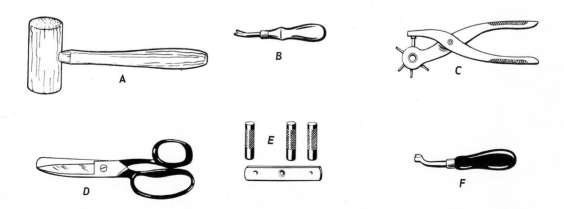

NEW WORDS FOR YOU TO USE

GRAIN (gran). The outer or hair side of a skin or hide, or the marking on that side.

TOOLING (tool - ing). To beautify vegetable-tanned leather by using certain tools to form or shape designs into the grain surface of the leather.

CONDITION (kon - dish - un). Addition of suitable amounts of water to vegetable-tanned leather so that it will readily respond to pressure made with leather tools in performing tooling or carving.

BEVEL (bev - el). To cut away sharp edges of leather to make the edges smooth and uniform.

TANNING (tan - ning). The process of converting animal pelts into leather by using chemicals obtained from certain tree barks, or by using metal chromium salt solutions.

PELT (pelt). Skin or hide removed from animals and preserved in preparation for tanning into leather.

HIDE (hid) As used in the leather industry, it refers to a whole pelt from one of the larger animals (cattle, horse, etc.).

SKIN (skin). The pelt from a young or small animal such as calf, sheep, goat, etc.

KIP (kip). Skin from an animal of the bovine species between the size of a calf and a matured animal. This term includes animals which have grown larger than those slaughtered for veal and certain undersize animals which may have reached maturity.

LEATHER PREPARATION, TANNING

1. How our ancestors made leather.
2. How leather is made today.
3. Animal pelts which are used.
4. Unit 2 projects.

ANCIENT METHOD OF TANNING

The pelts of animals killed for food were used by primitive people for clothing. The processes of tanning the skins were usually performed by the females of the tribes.

The ancient Hebrews are believed to be the first to discover the value of oak bark as a tanning agent. They seemed to be the most skilled of the early producers of leather and probably acquired the beginnings of their art from the Egyptians.

EARLY AMERICAN TANNING METHODS

Our ancestors prepared vats, sunk them in the ground, and filled them with a solution of lime and water. They placed pelts of animals in the solution to loosen hair and facilitate the scraping process. The pelts were then removed from the solution and carefully scraped by hand to remove the hair.

Oak bark crushed with stones was used by our colonists as a tanning agent. The scraped pelts were packed into vats in layers separated with finely crushed oak bark, filled with water, and left for six months or more. Fatty materials were then added to the hides to restore the natural oils removed during the tanning process.

EARLY AMERICAN INDUSTRY

Our colonists used large amounts of locally made leather because of the high cost of leather articles imported from Europe.

The tanneries of our early colonists were small and were operated by hand methods. They were established near the source of tanning materials. When tanning supplies became exhausted the tanneries were dismantled and moved to new sources of supply.

The demand for leather increased with the growth of the colonies until by the end of the seventeenth century there were several hundred tanneries. These were operated by men who had learned the trade in Europe or who had served apprenticeships in local plants.

MECHANIZATION OF EARLY AMERICAN INDUSTRY

Early in the nineteenth century, machines were developed for the tanning industry. One of the first machines was a splitting machine. This machine could split a hide into almost any desired thickness. The splits obtained were called "grain" from the hair side of the hide, and "flesh" from the flesh side.

Another important machine was one called an "unhairing" machine. This machine, as its name indicates, was used to remove hair or flesh from the skin or hide. The use of this machine reduced sharply the time required to do these jobs which in turn increased the production of the industry.

Other machines were developed and soon our country became one of the world's leading producers of leather. Machinery gradually replaced hand operations resulting in the establishment of large industries replacing the more numerous small industries.

Development of tanning concentrates and extracts eliminated the need for locating near sources of tanning materials. Improved transportation facilities permitted the hauling of raw materials to the industries at reduced cost. The large mechanized tanneries were able to produce more efficiently and economically than the small, hand operated ones. Consequently, the smaller tanneries began to disappear. Although the number of tanneries decreased, the value and size of their production increased.

MODERN SOURCES OF HIDES AND SKINS

Countries with vast grazing lands such as North and South America raise cattle for meat and dairy products, and are therefore the largest producers of hides and skins. Our country, with its extensive leather industry, is forced to import quantities of hides and skins to meet the demand. Argentina and Brazil furnish most of our needed cattle hides. The bulk of our imported kips come from Europe where consumption of veal and production of dairy cattle is high. The rare and expensive leathers we use, such as ostrich and reptile, come from Africa and other distant regions of the earth.

MODERN PREPARATION FOR TANNING

Pelt quality differs according to climatic conditions, season, and age of the animal.

Experts remove pelts from the animals used for meat. Great skill is necessary for a slip of the knife can greatly reduce the value of an entire hide.

After the pelts are removed they are spread out and salted to prevent bacteria and enzymes from attacking them. The salted pelts are preserved in three forms: (1) green salted pelts, salted and dried to 40 per cent moisture; (2) dry salted pelts, salted and dried to 10 per cent moisture; and (3) flint dried pelts, salted and thoroughly dried. The salted pelts are bundled and placed in a Hide House for storage

Hides and skins must be cleaned and made soft before other operations are undertaken. Clear water is used to wash away the salt. To hasten the softening process, the hides and skins are placed in drums and tumbled similar to the way we dry clothes with a mechanical dryer. Dirt, salt and blood are quickly removed, and the pelts become soft and clean. In the case of dry salted stock, the soaking time must be extended. When flint dry skins are handled, chemicals such as borax and sal soda are sometimes added. The length of time the hides must soak may be several days.

After the skins have become perfectly soft, they are placed between the rollers of a fleshing machine. A fleshing machine is equipped with a sharp spiral knife which revolves at a high rate of speed. The knife removes any remaining fat and flesh.

Hair must be removed to expose that part of the skin we call the grain side. The skin is placed in a tumbler containing a solution of water, lime and sodium

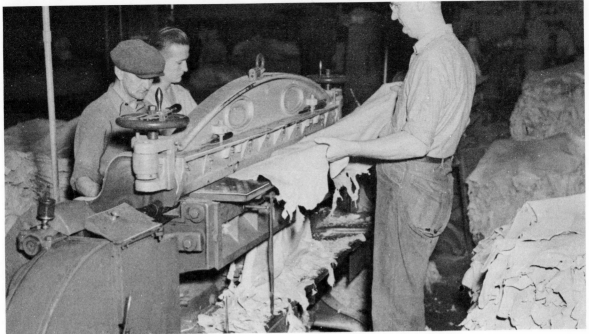

Fig. 2-1. Splitting leather.

sulphide. The time of the treatment varies, but the action is usually completed in three or four days. The solution causes the skin to swell and its pores to open, permitting easy penetration of chemicals. These chemicals act on the hair roots causing the hair to loosen.

Loosened hair is removed from the skin with an unhairing machine. It is similar to a fleshing machine except that the spiral knife is blunt instead of sharp.

Previously we mentioned that the chemicals used to prepare the skin for unhairing caused it to become swollen. This swelling gives the skin a rubbery condition which must be reduced and the skin brought again to a soft condition before it can be tanned. This is accomplished with a chemical process called "bating." The bating solution is prepared with such chemicals as sal ammoniac and pancreatic trypsin (dried pancreas) mixed with cornmeal. When the skin is taken from the bating solution it has lost its rubbery condition and has become silky-soft. In this condition it would quickly decompose if proper action is not taken.

From the bating drum the skin is placed in a vat containing a solution of common salt, sulphuric acid and water. This solution is referred to as the "pickle." Upon removal from the pickle, the skin has lost its silky condition and has assumed a leathery feel. The skin may be kept in this condition for some time, or sent to a tanner for further treatment.

MODERN METHODS OF TANNING

Vegetable Tanning

"TANNIN," the agent used in the process of vegetable tanning, is extracted from certain tree barks such as oak, hemlock, chestnut, quebracho and others. The TANNIN is extracted by a method known as leaching, similar to brewing coffee. Quebracho, our principal source of tanning agent for vegetable tanning, is imported from South America. Depletion in the supply of oak and hemlock bark, and destruction of chestnut wood by blight has curtailed our local supply.

We need a vegetable tanned leather for "tooling" or "CARVING." This will absorb water readily and will allow us to tool or carve it as we choose. This process is also preferred for tanning shoe-sole leather, because a thicker leather may be produced.

This process of tanning is long and expensive, often requiring three months or more.

Chrome Tanning

Near the end of the nineteenth century a new tanning process was perfected in our country. It was discovered that compounds of metal chromium produced leather different from that manufactured previously.

Chrome tanned leathers are more durable and stronger than vegetable tanned leathers but are not suitable for tooling, carving, or stamping. This method tightens the pores of leather making it water resistant.

Leathers are cheaper to produce with the chrome tanning method than with the vegetable tanning process.

Almost all the leather used for shoe uppers, gloves, and garments is processed by the chrome tanning method.

Chrome Tanning Process

Hides or skins to be tanned are hung on racks, then placed in vats containing a weak tanning solution. Every few days the hides are moved to vats containing stronger solutions. Into large drum-like tanks several hundred pickled hides are placed where they are turned and saturated with chrome salt solutions. The hides are then placed in a tumbler for rinsing.

After the rinsing process, excess moisture is removed from the hides. The hides are checked for thickness, and

often shaved with spiral cutting blades to make them more uniform.

Heavy hides are separated into splits. The hide is split lengthwise by a machine having a razor-sharp band knife which runs over two pulleys. It is fed to the knife with guide rollers and emerges on the opposite side as two separate pieces. The split coming from the upper side of the skin is called the grain split and the other the flesh split. (Fig. 2-1).

Fatty materials are added to the hides to replace the natural oils removed during the tanning process. The hides are then placed in dark, humid, and well ventilated rooms for drying.

Fig. 2-2. Calfskin.

During the processes of unhairing, wetting, tanning and drying the leather has become toughened. The staking operation softens the leather and makes it pliable.

KINDS OF CRAFT LEATHER

Our choice of leather for projects in leathercraft depends on how we intend to use it. A fine-grained leather is excellent for tooled billfolds, while a coarse-grained and more durable leather is better suited for making key cases, knife cases, ax sheaths, etc.

Descriptions of leathers commonly used for leathercraft projects follow.

In the accompanying photos, the grain of the leather has been exaggerated by enlargement to show detail.

CALFSKIN. You will find that the fine grain of calfskin makes it fine for tooling. Calfskin is especially well suited for making such items as coin purses and billfolds. It comes in a variety of colors. See Fig. 2-2.

Fig. 2-3. Steerhide.

COWHIDE. The soft finish of cowhide makes it suitable for tooling, carving, and stamping. You can purchase both light weight and heavy weight cowhide. The light weight cowhide is highly desir-

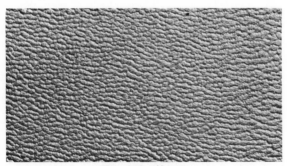

Fig. 2-4. Morocco.

able for small projects, especially where durability is desired, as in key cases. The heavy weight leather is excellent for belts and ax sheaths.

STEERHIDE. Steerhide is ideal for making beautiful and durable tooled projects. The crinkle grained finish of steerhide permits interesting effects even with plain designs such as shown in Fig. 2-3.

MOROCCO. This leather is made of goatskin. It was originally imported from Morocco, but is now obtained mostly from India. Its grain has a rich crinkled texture which is often imitated on other leathers, Fig. 2-4.

PIGSKIN. Although pigskin is toolable, its texture makes beautiful projects in the natural state, Fig. 2-5.

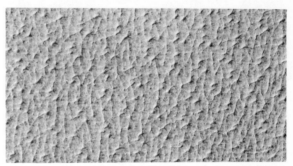

Fig. 2-5. Pigskin.

SHEEPSKIN. The reasonable cost of sheepskin makes it a good substitute for other toolable leathers. It is quite satisfactory for small projects.

HAIRCALF. Very young or unborn calf (slunk) is used to produce haircalf. The hair is left on the skin during the tanning process. You can make beautiful small projects with haircalf, Fig. 2-6.

Fig. 2-6. Haircalf.

ALLIGATOR. Natural embossed grain designs on alligator skins make extremely attractive projects. It is a non-tooling leather, but is very durable. See Fig.

2-7. Alligator-grain is often imitated on calfskin and sealskin.

SKIVER. This is a thin split of leather, generally used for linings. Skiver is

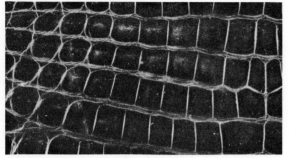

Fig. 2-7. Alligator.

Fig. 2-8. Skiver.

skin and calfskin are commonly used for making suede. Fig. 2-9.

usually made of sheepskin, calfskin, or cowhide, Fig. 2-8.

SUEDE. A tanned skin with the flesh side rubbed into a nap. This is usually done with buffing wheels. The soft velvet-like texture of suede makes it excellent as a lining material. It is non-toolable, but is ideal for small projects. Sheep-

Fig. 2-9. Suede.

PENCIL CASE, COMB CASE, BOOK MARK, COASTER OR PAPER WEIGHT, BLOTTER CORNER, GLASSES CASE
(Unit 2 Projects)

The projects in this unit require a little more time and material than the projects described in Unit 1.

By making a project in this unit you have an opportunity to learn new PROCESSES and to practice some of the processes you used in making Unit 1 projects. Try to pick a project which you really need, and then see how well you can make it. Perhaps you wish to make a project for a friend or a relative? Remember, you can increase the value of your project with good workmanship. You can save time and money by avoiding mistakes.

TOOLS REQUIRED

Pencil, scissors, skiving knife, skife, straight edge, small sponge or rag, tracing tool, modeling tool, one and four-prong thonging chisels, snap button set, revolving spring punch, mallet, edge beveler, and edge creaser.

MATERIALS REQUIRED

Tooling Cowhide. (described in Unit 1)

Rubber Cement.

Special preparations of cement are

Fig. 2-10. Suggested projects, Unit 2.

manufactured for use in leather work. You can easily apply rubber cement with a brush. It dries rapidly. The cement remains pliable when dry. Rubber cement will hold most porous materials firm, making it adaptable to leather, paper, and cardboard. You should spread it evenly to both surfaces to be joined, and allow it to dry before pressing the pieces together. A dull appearance is a good indication that rubber cement is dry. If a bit should be spilled onto the table on which you work, it may be brushed away easily when dry.

Tracing Paper

A piece of transparent paper is used in preparing designs to be transferred onto leather. Onionskin paper is excellent for this use.

Lacing

Both leather and plastic lacing are

materials suitable for leather projects. See Fig. 2-11. You will use lacing to assemble the parts of your leather projects. It is also used for decoration. Lacing is usually sold in 3/32 and 1/8 in. widths.

Fig. 2-11. Leather lacing (left), plastic lacing (right).

Leather lace is very durable and decorative. Goatskin and calfskin are popular lacing materials.

Plastic lace is durable, too, and is

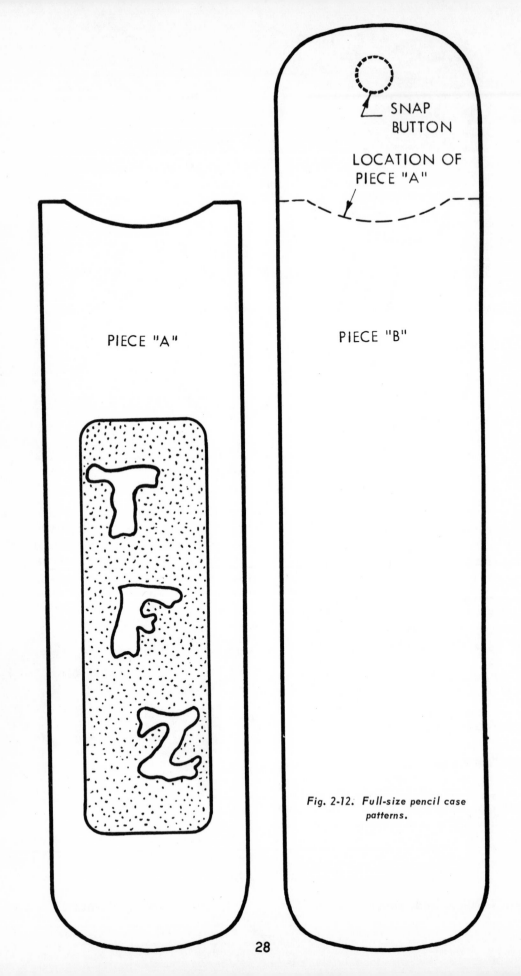

SNAP
BUTTON

LOCATION OF
PIECE "A"

PIECE "A"

PIECE "B"

Fig. 2-12. Full-size pencil case
patterns.

28

Fig. 2-13. Completed pencil case.

more economical than leather lacing. Plastic lace is made in a variety of colors.

Accessories (snap button.) Same as described for Unit 1.

Finishes. Same as described for Unit 1 projects.

PROJECT ANALYSIS

Select a Unit 2 project that you would like to make. You may wish to make a project of your own design using similar processes. On a separate sheet of paper list the processes necessary to make your project, arranging them in logical order. Refer to the job analysis chart, Fig. 1-1, page 7.

PROCEDURE FOR MAKING PROJECTS IN UNIT 2--PENCIL CASES, COMB CASES, BOOK MARKS, COASTERS OR PAPER WEIGHTS, BLOTTER CORNERS, AND GLASSES CASE

The illustrations show the step-by-step procedure for making the pencil case, Figs. 2-12 and 2-13. The directions for making other projects in this unit are nearly identical.

PENCIL CASE

Procedure:
1. Make the templates, using patterns given in Fig. 2-12.
2. Transfer the templates to leather.

Fig. 2-14. Cutting leather with a skiving knife.

(Step 2, Unit 1).
3   Cut leather with a skiving knife and straight edge, Fig 2-14.

Using uniform pressure, cut the leather with a sharp skiving knife. Use a straight edge as a cutting

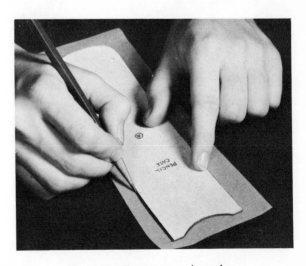

Fig. 2-15. Tracing around template onto tracing paper.

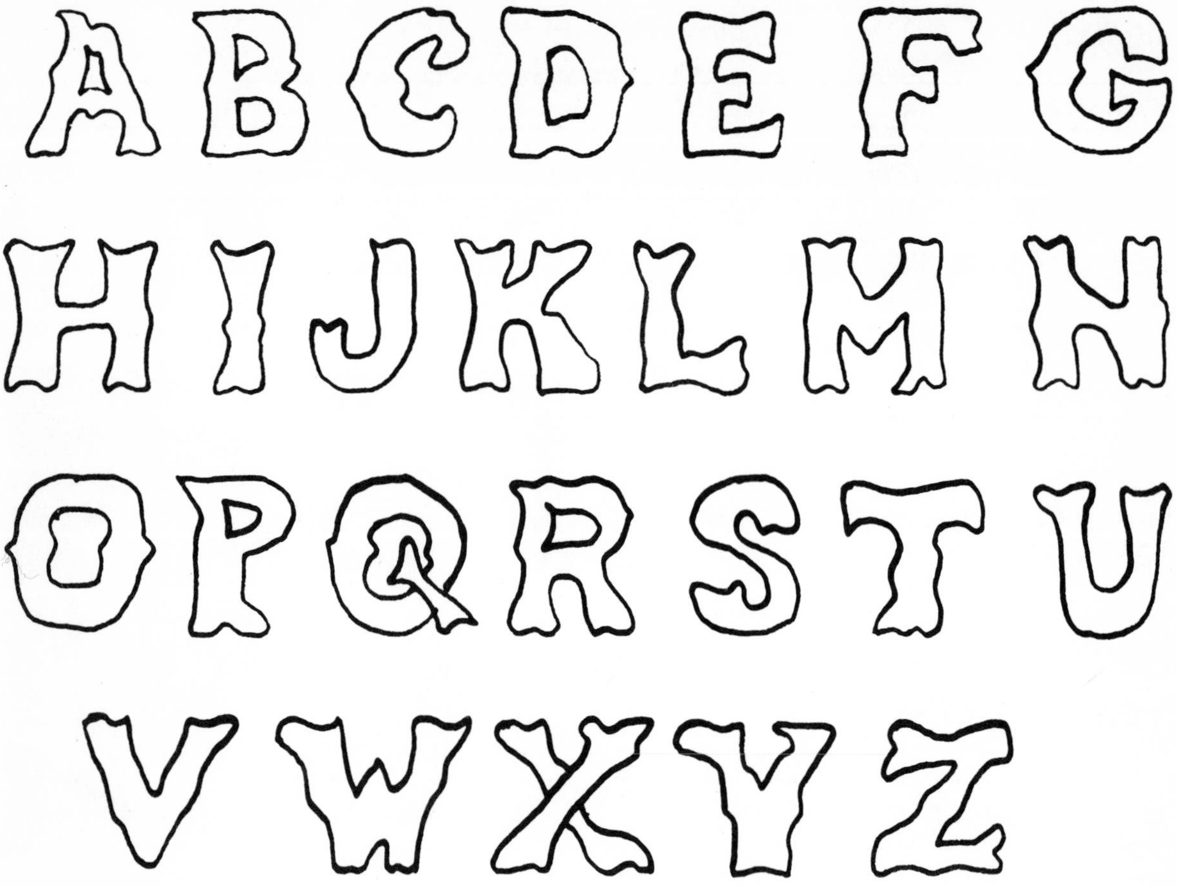

A B C D E F G H I J K L M N O P Q R S T U V W X Y Z

Fig. 2-16. Alphabet for leather projects.

guide. To help prevent slipping, first make light cuts, then cut deeper into the leather, using firm pressure

Fig. 2-17. Transferring design to leather.

on the knife.

4. Cut leather with scissors (Step 3, Unit 1).

5. Prepare a monogram or design.
   a. Draw a line around your template made from drawing A, Fig. 2-12, on a piece of tracing paper, Fig. 2-15.
   b. Trace or draw a monogram or design on the tracing paper in the same location as desired on the pencil case leather. See Fig. 2-16.
6. Condition the leather (Step 5, Unit 1).
7. Transfer your monogram or design to leather, Fig. 2-17.
   a. Transfer your monogram or design, using the tracing end of a spoon and tracer modeling tool. Tracing paper can be held over the leather with small pieces of masking tape. A piece of scrap marble or a piece of heavy plate glass makes a good backplate.
   b. Remove the tracing paper from the leather. Trace your design deeper

into the leather with a tracing tool, or with the tracing end of a spoon and tracer modeling tool, Fig. 2-18.

Fig. 2-18. Using tracing tool to trace design deeper into leather.

8. Model.
   Press down the leather around your initials or design with the spoon end of a spoon and tracer modeling tool, Fig. 2-19. This will cause your

Fig. 2-19. Using spoon end of tool to press down background around monogram.

monogram or design to stand out.
9. Background with a tracing tool.
   Hold the tracing end of a spoon and tracer modeling tool in a vertical position, and press it down with

firm and uniform pressure throughout the background of your design. Fig. 2-20.
10. Skife.
    Using a skife or a skiving knife, remove a thin layer of leather from

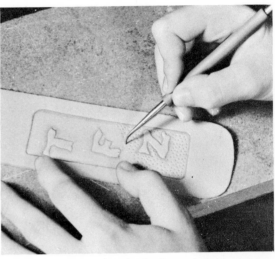

Fig. 2-20. Forming background design with tracing tool.

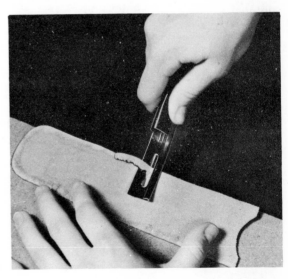

Fig. 2-21. Skiving edge of leather, using a skife.

all edges you are to join. Pare the edges down to about half their original thickness. This process of thinning the edges of leather helps to give your project a neat appearance. See Figs. 2-21 and 2-22.

11. Cement the edges to be joined together.

Apply a liberal coat of rubber ce-

edges, to be thonged (punched) for lacing. You may do this with a double-line marking tool, Fig. 2-24, or with a pair of dividers.

Fig. 2-22. Skiving with a knife.

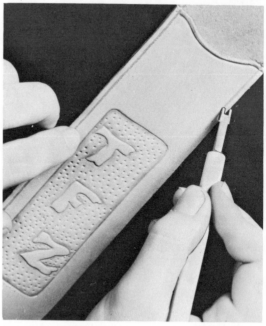

Fig. 2-24. Marking a line as a guide for thonging.

ment to both surfaces, Fig. 2-23.

12 Assemble the leather parts.

Press the cemented edges of piece A to piece B.

13. Thong.

a. Mark a line about 1/8 in. from the

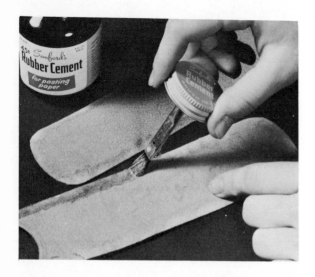

Fig. 2-23. Cementing edges to be joined.

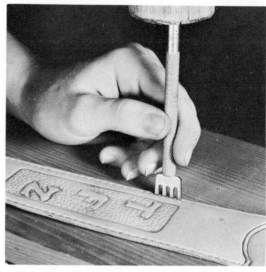

Fig. 2-25. Using a 4-prong thonging chisel.

b. Place a board with a smooth surface under your project to prevent marring your bench.

c. Start at a corner with 4-prong thonging chisel held in vertical position. Tap the thonging chisel with a wooden mallet being careful not to punch too deep. Use a one-prong or three-prong chisel to thong around the curves of your project. See Fig. 2-25.

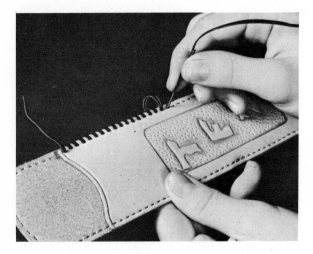

Fig. 2-26. Pencil case being laced with a single whip stitch.

14. Lace with a whip stitch. Choose between a single whip stitch, Fig. 2-27, and a cross whip stitch, Fig. 2-28.

a. Lace with a single whip stitch, Figs. 2-26 and 2-27.

To determine the approximate amount of lace you will need, measure the distance around your project and triple this measurement.

(1) Open two or three lacing slits with a tracing tool, fid, or a similar pointed tool.

(2) Sharpen both ends of the lace with a knife or a pair of scissors.

(3) Place the working end of the lace through the first hole from the back side of the leather, and pull lace toward you. Leave about an inch of lace as indicated at B, Fig. 2-27.

(4) Place the working end over the edge of the leather and go through the next hole. Move from left to right.

(5) Continue over the edge and through the hole in succeeding

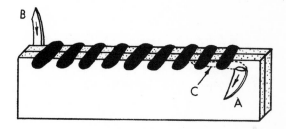

Fig. 2-27. Single whip stitch lacing procedure.

stitches. When all stitches are complete, tuck the ends of the lace under the stitches as indicated by detail at C, Fig. 2-27.

b. Lacing with a cross whip stitch is shown in Fig. 2-28.

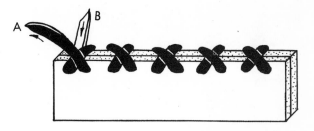

Fig. 2-28. Lacing with a cross whip stitch.

To determine the amount of lace you will need, measure the distance around your project and multiply by four.

(1) Open two or three lacing slits with a tracing tool, fid, or a similar pointed tool.

(2) Sharpen both ends of the lace with a knife or a pair of scissors.

(3) Place the working end of the lace through the first hole from the back side of the leather and pull the lace toward you. Leave about one inch of the lace as indicated at B, Fig. 2-28.

(4) Place the working end over the edge of the leather, skip one hole, and go through the next hole. Move from left to right.

(5) Continue over the edge of the leather and through every second hole on succeeding stitches.

(6) When the lacing reaches the beginning stitch, reverse the direction of the lacing and continue in the opposite direction.

(7) When you reach the beginning stitch, tuck the ends of the lace under the stitches as indicated for the single whip stitch at C, Fig. 2-27.

15. Attach a snap button. (Step 7, Unit 1)

16. Apply a finish (Step 8, Unit 1).

2. Transfer the templates to leather.
3. Cut leather with a skiving knife and a straight edge. Two pieces are required.
4. Cut leather with scissors.
5. Prepare a monogram or a design.
6. Condition the leather.
7. Transfer your monogram or design to leather.
8. Model.
9. Background with a tracing tool.
10. Skive.
11. Cement edges to be attached.
12. Assemble the leather parts.
13. Thong.
14. Lace with a whip stitch.
15. Apply finish.

Fig. 2-29. Completed comb case.

COMB CASE

Refer to project #1 for an explanation of these procedures:

1. Make the template, Fig. 2-30.

BOOK MARK

Procedure:
1. Make a template, Fig. 2-32.
2. Transfer the template to leather.
3. Cut leather with a skiving knife and a straight edge.
4. Prepare a monogram or a design.
5. Condition leather.
6. Transfer your monogram or design to leather.
7. Model.
8. Background with a tracing tool.
9. Bevel the edges.
10. Crease the edges.
11. Apply a finish.

Fig. 2-30. Pattern for comb case.

Fig. 2-32. Pattern
for book mark.

Completed projects. Above. Fig. 2-31. Bookmark.
Below. Fig. 2-33. Coaster and paper weight.

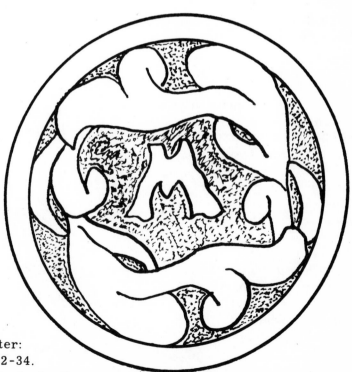

Fig. 2-34. Pattern for coaster and paper weight.

COASTER

Procedure for Making Coaster:

1. Make a template, Fig. 2-34.
2. Transfer the template to leather.
3. Cut leather with scissors, Step 3, Unit 1.

Fig. 2-35. Completed blotter corners.

4. Prepare a monogram or design.
5. Condition leather.
6. Transfer your monogram or design to leather.
7. Model.
8. Background with a tracing tool.
9. Bevel the edges, Step 4, Unit 1.
10. Crease the edges, Step 6, Unit 1.
11. Apply a finish.

PAPER WEIGHT

Procedure for Making Paper Weight:
1. Make the template, Fig. 2-34.
2. Transfer the template to leather.
3. Cut leather with scissors, unit 1, step 3. Two pieces are required.
4. Prepare a monogram or a design.
5. Condition leather.
6. Transfer monogram or design to leather.
7. Model.
8. Background with a tracing tool.
9. Skive.
10. Cement edges to be joined.
11. Assemble leather parts.
12. Thong.
13. Lace with a whip stitch.
14. Apply a finish.

BLOTTER CORNERS

1. Make the template, Fig. 2-36.
2. Transfer the template to leather.
3. Cut leather with a skiving knife and a straight edge.

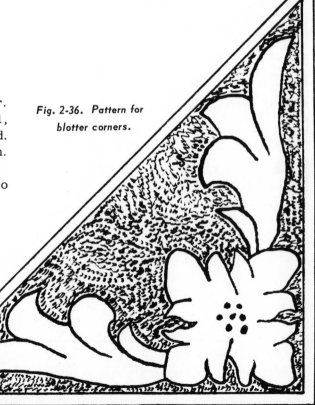

Fig. 2-36. Pattern for blotter corners.

4. Prepare a monogram or a design.
5. Condition the leather.
6. Transfer your monogram or design to leather.
7. Model.
8. Edge bevel. (Step 4, Unit 1)
9. Edge crease. (Step 6, Unit 1)
10. Background with a tracing tool.
11. Skive.
12. Cement the edges to be attached.
13. Assemble the leather parts.
14. Thong.
15. Lace with a whip stitch.
16. Apply a finish.

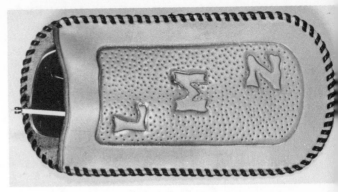

Fig. 2-37. *Completed glasses case.*

PIECE "B"

PIECE "A"

GLASSES CASE

1. Make the templates, Figs. 2-38, 2-39.
2. Transfer the template to leather.
3. Cut leather with a skiving knife and a straight edge.
4. Cut leather with scissors.
5. Prepare a monogram or a design.
6. Condition leather.
7. Transfer your monogram or design to leather.
8. Model.
9. Edge bevel. (Step 4, Unit 1)
10. Edge crease. (Step 6, Unit 1)
11. Background with a tracing tool.
12. Skive.
13. Cement the edges to be attached.
14. Assemble the leather parts.
15. Thong.
16. Lace with a whip stitch.
17. Apply a finish.

Fig. 2-38. *Piece A, pattern for glasses case.*

Fig. 2-39. *Piece B, pattern for glasses case.*

Fig. 2-40. Alternate designs for Unit 2.

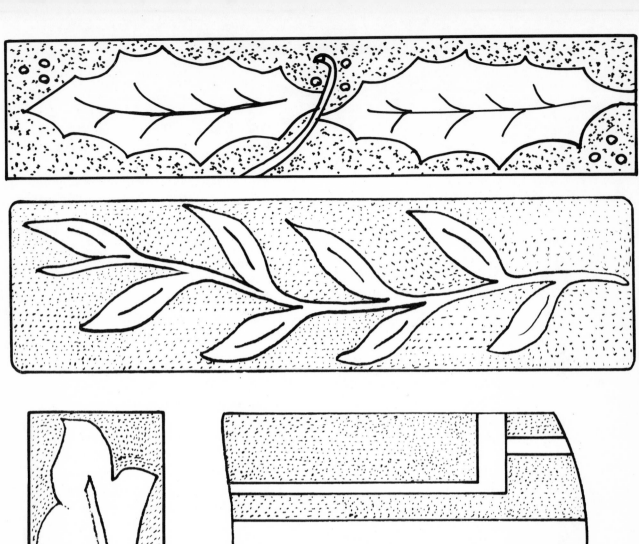

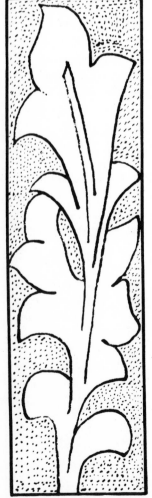

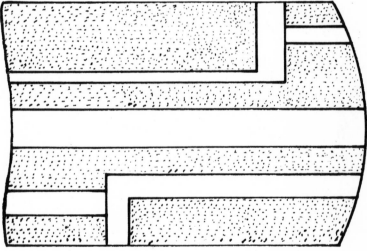

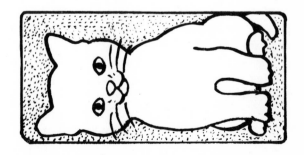

Fig. 2-41. More alternate designs for Unit 2.

QUIZ - UNIT 2

1. Vegetable tanned leather is preferable to chrome tanned leather for tooling and carving. True or false? Why?

2. Are leathers tanned by the chrome method cheaper or more expensive to produce than leathers made by vegetable tanning.

3. Tannin is extracted from certain tree barks by a process called batting, leaching, pickling or tanning.

4. In making shoe uppers, it is the usual custom to use chrome or vegetable tanned leather.

5. In splitting a hide (separating it into two splits) the split coming from the hair side of the skin is called the _____split, and the other the _____ split.

6. For what purposes is calfskin particularly well suited?

7. Give a brief description of haircalf leather.

8. Is alligator skin ordinarily tooled? Why?

9. Skiver leather is another name for sheepskin. True or false?

10. Suede leather is made of goatskin, a tanned skin with the flesh side rubbed into a nap, or is a thin split of cowhide.

11. What kind of cement is commonly used for assembling leathercraft projects?

12. Name two types of lacing. Which is the more expensive to buy?

13. Monograms are usually transferred onto leather with carbon paper and pencil. True or false?

14. Lacing slits are punched about_____ inch from the edges on most projects.

15. Pressing leather down around a monogram or design is called creasing, skiving, modeling, or thonging.

16. Why is leather thinned at the edges?

17. Two tools used for thinning edges of leather are _____.

18. The solution used to clean and bleach completed leather projects referred to in this Unit consists of 20 parts of water and one part of _____.

19. What are two methods of lacing with a whip stitch?

20. Describe what we mean by thonging a project.

NEW WORDS FOR YOU TO USE

Analysis (a - nal - i - sis). Separation of anything into its parts or elements and an examination of these parts.

Monogram (mon - o - gram). Two or more letters or designs used together to represent a name.

Design (de - zin). To make a plan for a project or arrangement of details in a plan.

Tannin (tan - in). A substance (tannic acid) obtained from certain tree barks which is needed to tan pelts into leather suitable for tooling or carving.

Carving (karv - ing). To cut through the grain surface of leather, separating the leather fibers, so that tooling or stamping of the leather may be easily accomplished.

FINISHING, MEASURING, GRADING LEATHER

1. Finishing and grading leather.
2. How leather differs from other materials produced for similar purposes.
3. How leather is sold.
4. Using a swivel knife.
5. Unit 3 Projects.

HOW LEATHER IS FINISHED

Natural leather (without color) is trimmed and ironed with heavy metal plates under several tons of pressure.

Smaller hides of leather to be colored are placed in huge drums containing dye and are tumbled. They are then stretched on racks and allowed to dry.

We can observe large hides being placed on screens and the color being sprayed on, in Fig. 3-1. All hides are ironed with plating machines after they are dyed.

A special graining effect is obtained by "boarding" leather. The leather is folded with the grain side in and the sur-

Fig. 3-1. Spraying dye on leather.
(Ohio Leather Company)

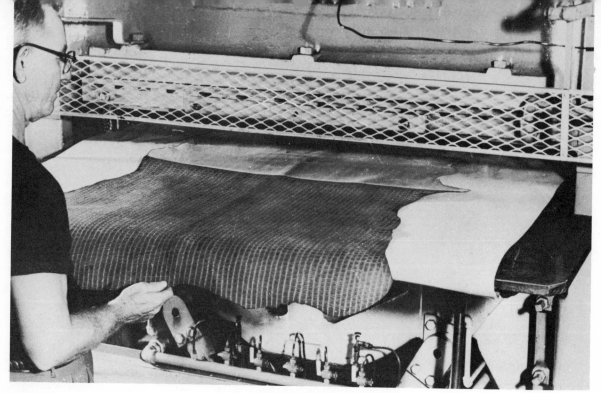

Fig. 3-2. Embossing leather.

faces rubbed together under pressure of a cork-surfaced instrument called a "hand board." Machinery is also used to board leather. Boarded leathers are not intended for tooling or carving.

Suede. We have all seen suede shoes. To produce a suede finish one must rub the flesh side of leather into a fine nap with a buffing wheel. Oscillating buffing machines are used to further refine and smooth out the skin for a high grade suede finish. We frequently use suede finished leather, usually sheepskin, as lining material.

Embossed leathers. Heavy plating machines which press designs on leather surfaces produce the embossed leather we use in our country. Refer to Fig. 3-2. The designs are usually used to imitate the grain of leather from other animals, such as alligator on steer and pigskin on sheep. "Levant" is a term used to describe a grain pattern sometimes given to goat and sheep skins.

Glazed. We can obtain a high gloss finish with glass rollers. Modern finishes sprayed on leathers will also produce a glazed appearance. Glazed leathers are not suitable for tooling.

HOW LEATHER IS MEASURED

Complicated machines used to measure leather eliminate all the guess work. Every square inch is accounted for, even the area of holes in the leather is subtracted, as the machine measures. Leather measuring machines, Fig. 3-3, are periodically checked by government inspectors, for accuracy.

Sizes are marked on the back of the hides. Sizes of hides are given to the nearest 1/4 sq. ft.

HOW LEATHER IS GRADED

No machine has yet been invented that will grade leather. Grading is done by experts who are trained in the art of judging leather quality and can tell the value of leather by sight and feel.

Some of the tanneries in our country grade leather by numbers 1, 2, 3, etc.,

Fig. 3-3. Leather being fed through measuring machine.

others by letters A, B, C, D, DX, etc. All grades of leather are tanned the same. The difference is mostly in the number of scratches, blemishes, holes, brand marks, and stains.

Only a very small percentage of hides are grade A. Therefore, the price for grade A leather is high.

LEATHER SUPPLY

Many leathercrafters prefer buying B or C grades of leather because of the reduced cost. They can usually cut around imperfections, when making small projects. Designs can be planned so that blemishes are tooled out when making larger projects.

You can purchase leather from hundreds of companies throughout the nation. Leather is sold in several ways.

(1) Full-skin or half-skin. This method gives you an opportunity to experience more processes and it is the most economical way to buy leather.

(2) Even square feet. Leather is more expensive when purchased by even square feet, but with careful planning you will have less waste.

(3) One or five pound packages. Should you wish to buy leather in small quantities, this method affords a greater variety of color and kinds of leather; and is usually excellent for small projects.

(4) Kit form. You can purchase ready-cut leather projects, together with other necessary materials to complete them, including designs. This method is useful if you are purchasing for a small group such as a church or club group and time and working space are limited.

LEATHER CHARACTERISTICS

The properties which distinguish leather from other materials produced for similar purposes are its resilience, high tear strength, porosity, elasticity, and ease of fabrication.

Synthetic materials do not usually possess the superior qualities of leather, age with such mellowness, or look as expensive as leather. Many synthetic materials fade, crack, peel, and wear out quickly.

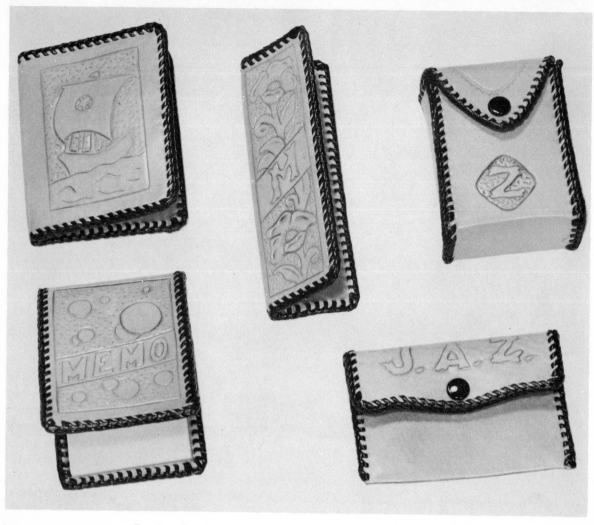

Fig. 3-4. Suggested Projects, Unit 3 - Picture and card holder, Nail
file and comb case, Cigarette case, Memo-pad cover, Coin purse.

PROCEDURES

In working with projects in Unit 2, you have used modeling tools to make your designs stand out. Let's now try the fascinating art of incising the design with a swivel knife. You will find that your use of the swivel knife to incise (cut about half way through the leather, following the design outline) will aid you in tooling since less pressure is necessary to press the leather down around your design.

The experience which you gained in making previous leather projects will help you give the projects of this group a real professional look. A well-made leather project will give years of service and a lot of self-satisfaction.

By making a project of this group you will have an opportunity to learn new leather-working procedures and to practice many of the processes with which you are already familiar.

You may wish to make a gift for a friend or relative. Perhaps you know of other projects that can be made by following the general outline of processes illustrated in this group. Originality of construction and design can make your projects of even more value to you and to others. Alternate design ideas are given at the end of this unit.

TOOLS REQUIRED

Pencil, skiving knife, skife, scissors, small sponge or rag, spoon and tracer modeling tool, swivel knife, deer's foot and double line marking tool, straight edge, edge beveler, edge creaser, embossing wheel and carriage, thonging chisel, mallet, revolving spring punch, snap button set, fid, lacing needle, dividers.

MATERIALS REQUIRED

Tooling calfskin or cowhide, 2-1/2-3 oz.
Tracing paper.
Rubber cement.
Accessories (snap button).
Lace.
Finishes.

PROJECT ANALYSIS

From the analysis chart, page 7, you can determine processes necessary to make Unit 3 projects. You may wish to design a project of your own requiring similar processes. On a separate sheet of paper list the processes necessary to make your project, then arrange them in logical order.

PROCEDURES FOR MAKING COIN PURSES, PICTURE AND CARD HOLDERS, CIGARETTE CASES, NAIL FILE AND COMB CASES, AND MEMO-PAD COVERS

Procedures illustrated for this group show the making of a coin purse. See Fig. 3-5. The procedures described for making the coin purse are applicable to making all Unit 3 projects.

1. Make the templates. Figs. 3-6 and 3-7. (Step 1, Unit 1).
2. Transfer the templates to leather.
3. Cut leather with a skiving knife and straight edge. (Step 3, Unit 2)
4. Cut leather with scissors. (Step 3, Unit 1)
5. Prepare your design and monogram (Step 5, Unit 2).

The designs included with this group of projects are only a few of the many possible ideas appropriate for use with these projects. Magazines and catalogs are other sources of design ideas. You can redraw designs obtained elsewhere to suit your particular projects.

Figure 3-8 is a partially completed design. You may want to complete this design for use with your project, or for practice. Try redrawing this design or

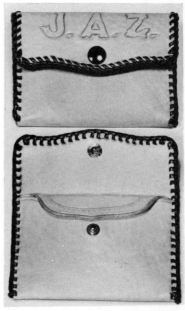

Fig. 3-5. Completed coin purse.

drawing one of your own on a separate sheet of paper to provide a suitable pattern for your project.

6. Condition the leather.
   The moisture content of your leather should be high for incising. Conditions vary according to weather conditions and leather thickness. In general, add moisture evenly to your leather until it has a darkened appearance. As soon as your leather begins to turn back to near its nor-

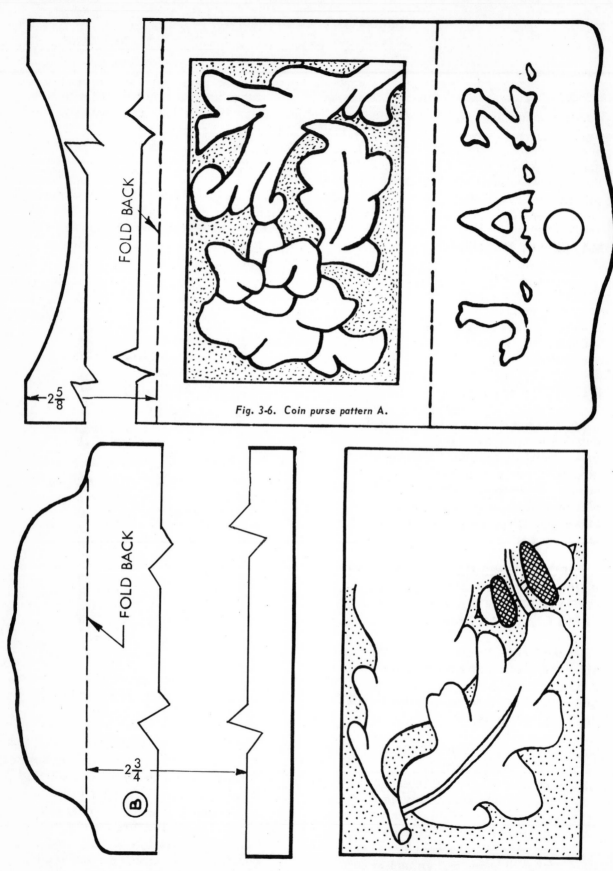

FOLD BACK

$2\frac{5}{8}$

J. A. Z.

Fig. 3-6. Coin purse pattern A.

FOLD BACK

$2\frac{3}{4}$

B

Fig. 3-7. Coin purse pattern B.

Fig. 3-8. Design to be redrawn and completed by student.

mal color you can begin carving. If time permits, wrap the dampened leather in a wet towel and leave it for several hours. This opens the pores and softens the fibers of the leather. When the leather is un-wrapped, allow the surface to return to near its normal color before carving. The leather will still be damp beneath the surface.

7. Transfer your design and monogram to leather. (Step 7, Unit 2)

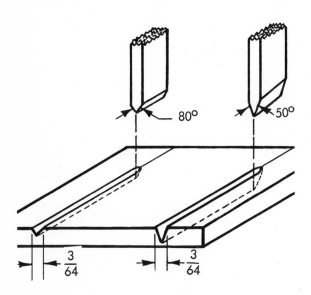

Fig. 3-9. Cuts made with swivel knife blades of wide and narrow angles.

8. Incise with a swivel knife.
   a. Incise a practice piece. See Fig. 3-9.
      (1) Select a small piece of leather of the same kind and thickness as that of your project, and practice to get the knack of using a swivel knife. In incising, you outline the design so the background right up to the design may be depressed with ease.
      (2) Condition the practice piece of leather.
      (3) Grasp the barrel of the swivel knife with your thumb and second finger.

      (4) Place your index finger over the saddle and rest your little finger on the surface of the leather to aid you in guiding the knife.
      (5) Tip the knife forward slightly to allow the point of the cutting edge at the front to do the cutting.
      (6) Hold the broad side of the blade at a right angle to the surface of the leather, Fig. 3-10. A blade held at less than 90 degrees will

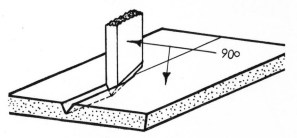

Fig. 3-10. Correct (wedgecut).

result in an undesirable under-cut, Fig. 3-11.
      (7) Cut only to a depth of about one-half the thickness of your leath-er.
   b. Incise your design.
      (1) Place the front point of the cut-

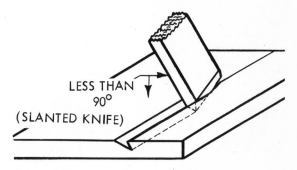

Fig. 3-11. Incorrect (wedgecut).

ting edge at the beginning of one of your design lines.
      (2) Following the design line closely, pull the knife toward you with uniform pressure, Fig. 3-12. Follow the curves in your design by turning the barrel between

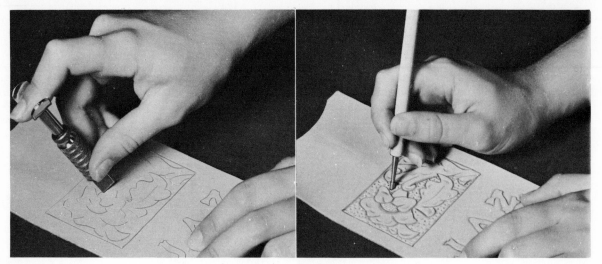

Fig. 3-12. Left. Incising design with swivel knife. Fig. 3-13.
Right. Using deer's foot tool to form backgroud decoration.

your fingers. At the end of each stroke, gradually release the pressure on the knife, resulting in a tapered cut. You can make the curved cuts in several steps, turning your leather to a new

Fig. 3-14. Marking line with dividers.

position after each cut. With practice, you can become proficient in cutting, turning, and tapering with smoothly executed movements.

(3) Use a straight edge as an aid in making straight cuts.

c. Try to prevent:

(1) Cutting across another cut.

(2) Re-cutting. Always cut to the desired depth with one cut.

(3) Using a dull knife. See page 90 for information on sharpening.

(4) Making undercuts. Hold your knife at right angles to the leather surface. DO NOT slant your knife to the left or right.

(5) Dry leather. Additional moisture should be used sparingly. Too much moisture added to incised leather tends to close up the cuts.

9. Model. (Step 8, Unit 2)

10. Background your design with a deer's foot tool or with a ball modeling tool.

Hold the deer's foot modeling tool in a vertical position and press it down with firm and uniform pressure throughout the background. The deer's foot modeling tool, as indicated by its name, has a half-oval shape similar to a deer's foot, Fig. 3-13.

11. Edge bevel the flap of the inside pocket. (Step 4, Unit 1)

12. Edge crease the flap of the inside pocket. (Step 6, Unit 1)

13. Emboss the flap of the inside pocket.

a. Using a pair of dividers or a compass, mark a line about 1/4 in. from the creased edge of the flap. Hold the point of one divider leg next to the creased edge of the flap as a guide. The other point will mark the leather when you apply pressure to the dividers, Fig. 3-14.

b. Using an embossing wheel, follow closely the line you made on the

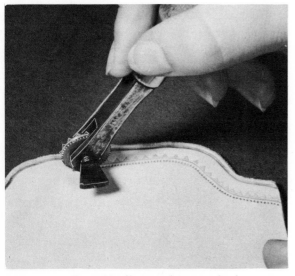

Fig. 3-15. *Using embossing wheel.*

flap with dividers. Push the embossing wheel in a forward direction with firm and uniform pressure, Fig. 3-15.

14. Skive (Step 10, Unit 2)

15. Cut grooves to make the folds.

a. Mark straight lines on the flesh side of piece A where you will make the folds, Fig. 3-6.

b. Using a gouge, cut grooves into the flesh side of piece A following the lines carefully. Cut the grooves to

a depth of about one-half the thickness of the leather. Push the gouge with firm and uniform pressure. These grooves will enable you to make neat and sharp folds in your project, Fig. 3-16.

16. Attach a skiver lining.

a. Apply a liberal coat of rubber cement to the flesh side of piece A, Fig. 3-17.

b. Cut out a piece of skiver the ap-

Fig. 3-16. *Cutting grooves with a gouge.*

proximate size and press it to the glued surface. You must be careful to avoid wrinkles. Begin at one end and gradually move toward the

Fig. 3-17. *Applying rubber cement to piece A.*

other end, pressing from the center toward the sides. Fold your project as you go to avoid slack. Slack will cause wrinkles, Fig. 3-17.

17. Trim the skiver lining.

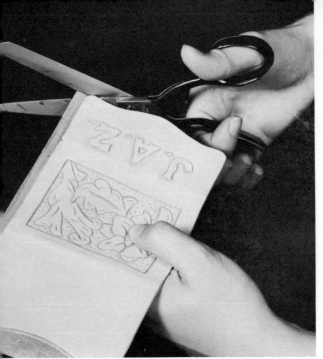

Fig. 3-18. Using scissors to trim skiver lining.

Trim off the excess lining material with a pair of scissors, Fig. 3-18

18. Cement the edges to be attached. (Step 11, Unit 2).
19. Assemble the leather parts.
20. Attach a snap button. (Step 7, Unit 1)

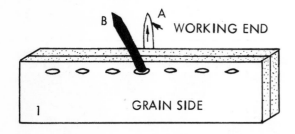

Fig. 3-19. Double buttonhole stitch, step 1.

21. Thong. (Step 13, Unit 1)
22. Lace with a double buttonhole stitch.
    To determine the amount of lace you will need, measure the distance around your project and multiply this by six. Begin lacing where the inside of your project is accessible. Sharpen both ends of the lace.

a. Step 1. Place the lace through the first hole from the front side of the leather, and pull the lace away from you. Leave about two inches of lace as indicated at B in step 1, Fig. 3-19.

b. Step 2. Bring the lace over the edge

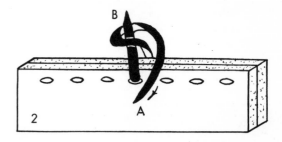

Fig. 3-20. Double buttonhole stitch, step 2.

of the leather and over the two inch piece of lace you left in step 1, Fig. 3-20.

c. Step 3. Place the working end through the next hole forming a cross in the lace, Fig. 3-21.

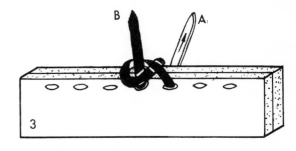

Fig. 3-21. Double buttonhole stitch, step 3.

d. Step 4. Bring the lace over the edge of the leather and through the cross from the front side, Fig. 3-22.

e. Step 5. Place the working end of

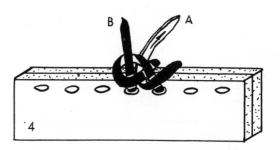

Fig. 3-22. Double buttonhole stitch, step 4.

the lace through the next hole from the front side of the leather forming another cross. Continue through the hole and through the cross until you reach the beginning stitch, Fig. 3-23.

f. Step 6. Remove the first two stitches

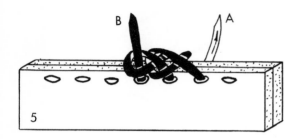

Fig. 3-23. Double buttonhole stitch, step 5.

leaving a loop and two open holes. Place the end of the lace through second hole, lacing from the back

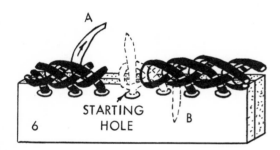

Fig. 3-24. Double buttonhole stitch, step 6.

side between the two leathers as indicated at B in step 6, Fig. 3-24.

g. Step 7. Lace the working end through the beginning hole and leave the

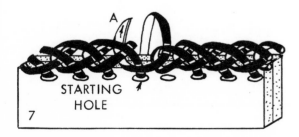

Fig. 3-25. Double buttonhole stitch, step 7.

cross open. Place the working end of the lace through the loop and through the cross, Fig. 3-25.

h. Step 8. Place the working end of the lace back down through the loop and through the front side of the remain-

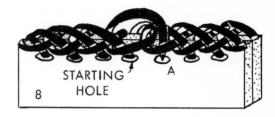

Fig. 3-26. Double buttonhole stitch, step 8.

ing hole. Pull the working end of the lace down between the two leathers. The lace is now complete, Fig. 3-26.

23. Apply a finish. (Step 8, Unit 1)

PICTURE AND CARD HOLDER

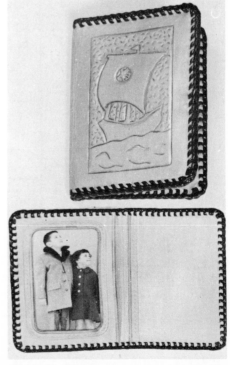

Fig. 3-27. Completed picture and card holder.

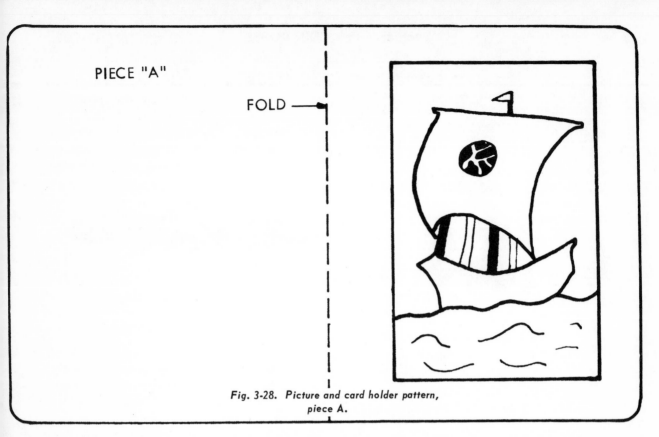

PIECE "A"

FOLD ——

*Fig. 3-28. Picture and card holder pattern,
piece A.*

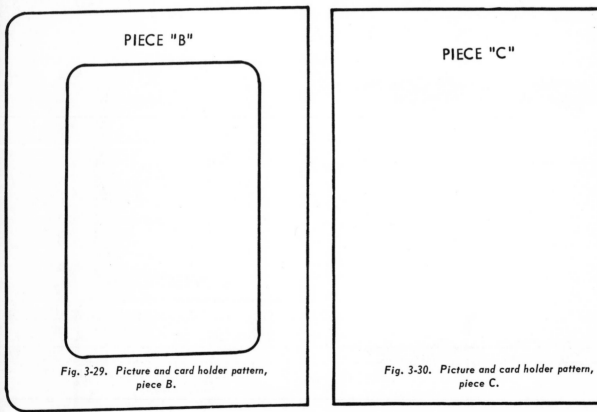

PIECE "B"

*Fig. 3-29. Picture and card holder pattern,
piece B.*

PIECE "C"

*Fig. 3-30. Picture and card holder pattern,
piece C.*

PICTURE AND CARD HOLDER

Procedure:

1. Make the templates, Figs. 3-28, 3-29, 3-30.
2. Transfer the templates to leather.
3. Cut leather with a skiving knife and straight edge.
4. Cut leather with scissors.
5. Prepare your design.
6. Condition the leather.
7. Transfer your design to leather.
8. Incise your design with a swivel knife.
9. Model.
10. Background your design with a deer's foot tool.
11. Bevel the edge of piece B and piece C which you will not attach or lace.
12. Crease the edge of piece B and piece C which you will not attach or lace.
13. Emboss the creased edge of piece B and piece C.
14. Skive.
15. Cut a groove to make a fold.
16. Attach a skiver lining.
17. Trim the skiver lining.
18. Cement the edges to be attached.
19. Assemble the leather parts.
20. Thong.
21. Lace with a double button hole stitch.
22. Apply a finish.

CIGARETTE CASE

Procedure:

1. Make the template, Fig. 3-32.
2. Transfer the templates to leather.
3. Cut leather with a skiving knife and straight edge.
4. Cut leather with scissors.
5. Prepare your design.
6. Condition the leather.
7. Transfer your design to leather.
8. Incise design with a swivel knife.
9. Model.
10. Background design with a deer'sfoot tool.
11. Bevel the edge which you will not attach or lace.
12. Crease the edge which you will not attach or lace.
13. Emboss the flap.
14. Skive.
15. Cut grooves to make the folds.
16. Attach a skiver lining.
17. Trim the skiver lining.
18. Cement the edges to be attached.
19. Assemble the leather parts.
20. Attach a snap button.
21. Thong.
22. Lace with a double button hole stitch.
23. Apply a finish.

Fig. 3-31. Completed cigarette case.

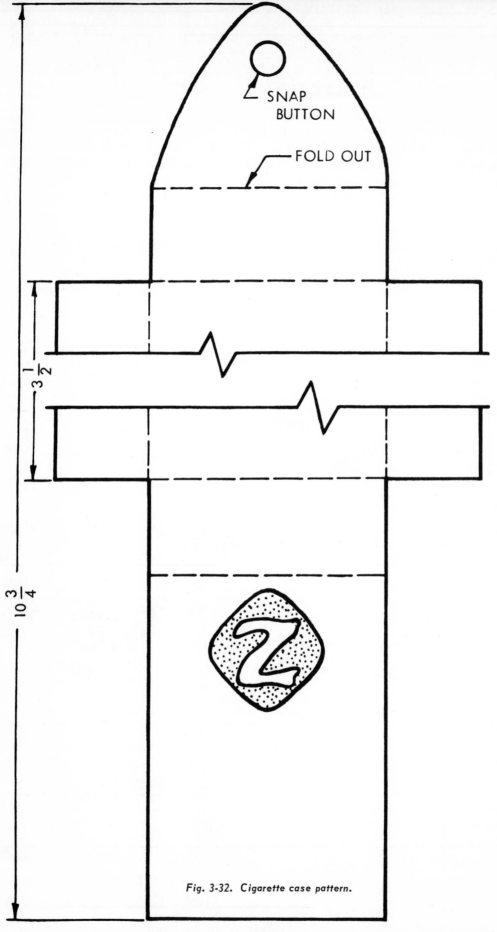

SNAP
BUTTON

FOLD OUT

$3\frac{1}{2}$

$10\frac{3}{4}$

Fig. 3-32. Cigarette case pattern.

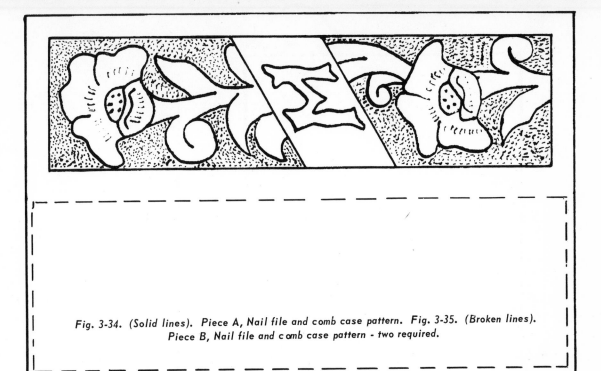

Fig. 3-34. *(Solid lines). Piece A, Nail file and comb case pattern.* Fig. 3-35. *(Broken lines).*
Piece B, Nail file and comb case pattern - two required.

NAIL FILE AND COMB CASE

Procedure:

1. Make the templates, Figs. 3-34 and 3-35.
2. Transfer the templates to leather.
3. Cut leather with a skiving knife and straight edge.
4. Prepare your designs.
5. Condition the leather.
6. Transfer your design to leather.
7. Incise your design with a swivel knife.
8. Model.
9. Background your design with a deer'sfoot tool.
10. Bevel the edge of piece B which you will not attach or lace.
11. Crease the edge of piece B which you will not attach or lace.
12. Emboss the creased edge of piece B.
13. Skive.
14. Cut grooves to make a fold.
15. Attach a skiver lining.
16. Trim a skiver lining.
17. Cement the edges to be attached.
18. Assemble the leather parts.
19. Thong.
20. Lace with a double button hole stitch.
21. Apply finish.

Fig. 3-33. *Completed nail file and comb case.*

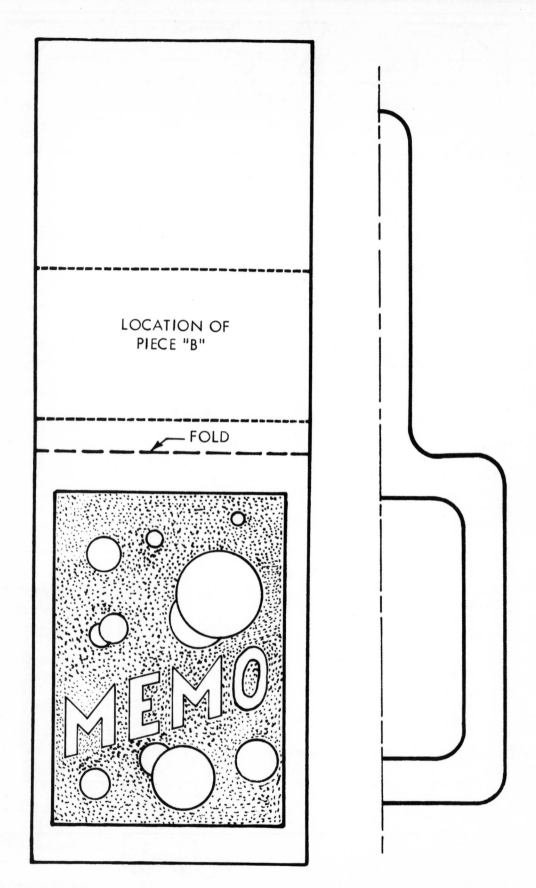

LOCATION OF
PIECE "B"

← FOLD

MEMO

Fig. 3-36. Left. Memo pad pattern, piece A. Right. Half-pattern for luggage tag, to be completed by student.

Fig. 3-37. Completed memo pad.

MEMO PAD

Procedure:
1. Make the templates, Figs. 3-36, 3-38.
2. Transfer the templates to leather.
3. Cut leather with a skiving knife and straight edge.
4. Prepare your design.
5. Condition the leather.
6. Transfer your design to leather.
7. Incise your design with a swivel knife.
8. Model.
9. Background your design with a deer's foot tool.
10. Bevel the edges of piece B which you will not attach or lace.
11. Crease the edges of piece B which you will not attach or lace.
12. Emboss the creased edges of piece B.
13. Skive.
14. Cut grooves to make a fold.
15. Attach a skiver lining.
16. Trim the skiver lining.
17. Cement the edges to be attached.
18. Assemble the leather parts.
19. Thong.
20. Lace with a double button hole stitch.
21. Apply finish.

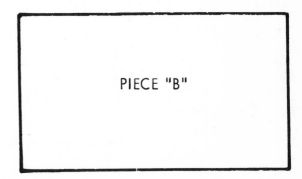

PIECE "B"

Fig. 3-38. Memo pad pattern, piece B.

Fig. 3-39. Alternate design suggestions for Unit 3.

Fig. 3-40. Design suggestions. Left.
Checkbook cover. Right. Billfold.

QUIZ - UNIT 3

1. In producing a suede finish on leather, the _____ side is rubbed into a fine nap with a buffing wheel.

2. Name four properties of leather that distinguish it from synthetic materials used for similar purposes.

3. Which is the top grade of leather, A, B, or C? Which grade will wear best?

4. Four ways leather is sold are: _____ .

5. Leather with a high gloss finish produced on its grain surface with glass rollers is called embossed leather, glazed leather, suede leather, or boarded leather.

6. The use of a swivel knife to cut into leather through its grain side is called _____ .

7. Even though no leather is actually removed, the swivel knife is often referred to as a _____ knife.

8. The moisture content of leather should be low for incising. True or false?

9. The tool recommended to background designs of Unit 3 is the spoon and tracer modeling tool; deer's foot tool; stippler; tracing tool.

10. You should incise your design with a swivel knife by cutting to a depth of about 1/8 the thickness of your leather; 1/4 the thickness of your leather; 1/2 the thickness of your leather; 2/3 the thickness of your leather.

11. When incising your design, you should hold the broad side of the swivel knife blade at 30 degrees to the surface of the leather; 45 degrees to the surface of the leather; 60 degrees to the surface of the leather; 90 degrees to the surface of the leather.

12. To properly hold the swivel knife, you should grip it with your index finger at a position near the handle; over the yoke; on the barrel; near the blade.

13. The lacing stitch recommended for projects of this group is called the single whip stitch; cross whip stitch; single button hole stitch; double button hole stitch.

14. Edges of leather projects which have been rounded with an edge creaser may be further decorated with an edge beveler; a deer's foot tool; an embossing wheel; a stippler.

15. If excessive moisture is added to the leather after the carving is begun, the result is likely to be that the cuts will close up; the cuts will widen; water spots will appear; the leather will stretch.

16. Identify these tools: A, B, C, D, E, F.

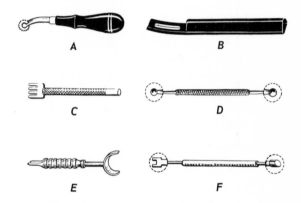

NEW WORDS FOR YOU TO USE

1. Emboss (em - bos). To beautify leather by stamping, pressing or rolling designs into its grain surface. Vegetable-tanned leather must be used.

2. Glaze (glaz). A finish produced by polishing the grain surface of tanned leather under heavy pressure of glass or steel rollers. Infrequently made with varnish or shellac coating.

3. Levant (le - vant). This term means crushed. It is used to define the natural grain pattern on skins of certain species of goat. It is also used to describe a grain pattern imitated on goat, sheep, and seal skins.

STAMPING, CARVING, DECORATING LEATHER

UNIT 4

1. Stamps to use in beautifying carved designs.
2. Purposes for which gussets are used.
3. Ornamenting leather designs with filigree.
4. Design suggestions.
5. Unit 4 Projects.

TOOLS FOR STAMPING AND CARVING

Stamping tools, sometimes called saddle stamps, are used extensively in beautifying projects made of vegetable-tanned leather. Most saddle stamps are used to decorate leather after it has been carved or incised. Fig. 4-1 illustrates some of the tools available, stored in a rack. Figs. 4-2 and 4-3 will help you to identify stamping tools described here and to recognize the impressions made with some of the many available saddle stamps. Note also the "how-to" drawings on page 4.

CAMOUFLAGE TOOLS

The camouflage tool has a convex and a concave edge and is shaped like a crescent. It is sometimes referred to as a "sunburst." Evenly spaced lines run from the inside of the crescent to its outside, Fig. 4-2.

The camouflage tool is used to decorate stems, leaves, flower petals, and fern swirls. See Fig. 4-11. Its impression results in a ruffled appearance representing veins and folds. The camouflage stamp is available in several sizes.

PEAR SHADERS

The pear shader is shaped like a tear

drop or pear. It is available in several sizes. This stamp may be purchased with a smooth burnishing surface or with a textured surface. See Fig. 4-2.

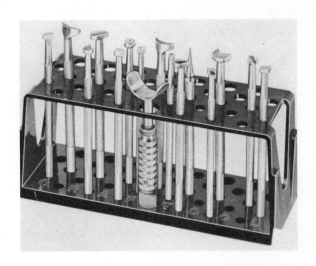

Fig. 4-1. An assortment of saddle stamps.

The pear shader is used to produce dish or bowl-shaped impressions (contour shading) in flower petals and leaves, giving them a three-dimensional appearance, as in Fig. 4-12. When used correctly, the deep impressions you make with the pear shader will have a contrasting darker color giving the leather a shaded appearance; leaves and flower petals in your design will seem to come to life. You may prefer lined and checked

61

CRAFTOOL

Chrome Plated Steel Saddle Stamps

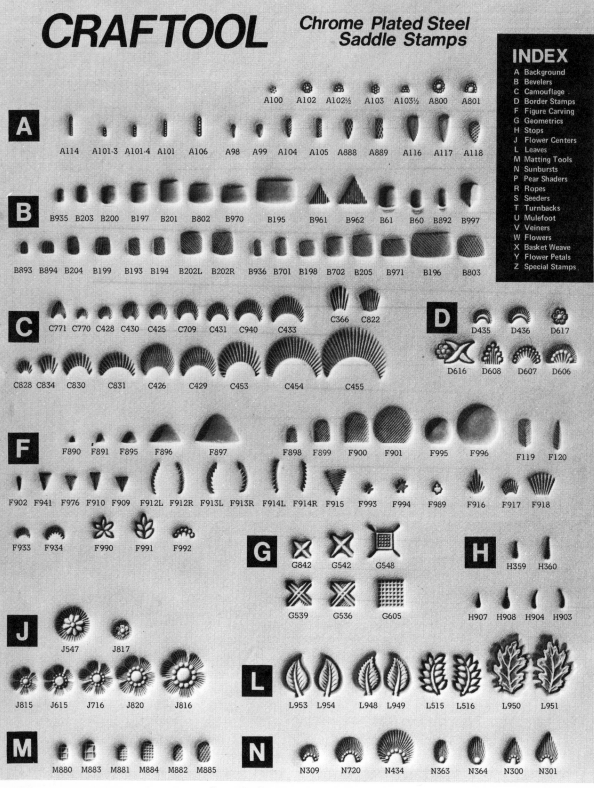

INDEX

A Background
B Bevelers
C Camouflage
D Border Stamps
F Figure Carving
G Geometrics
H Stops
J Flower Centers
L Leaves
M Matting Tools
N Sunbursts
P Pear Shaders
R Ropes
S Seeders
T Turnbacks
U Mulefoot
V Veiners
W Flowers
X Basket Weave
Y Flower Petals
Z Special Stamps

Fig. 4-2. Stamping tool impressions.
(The Craftool Company)

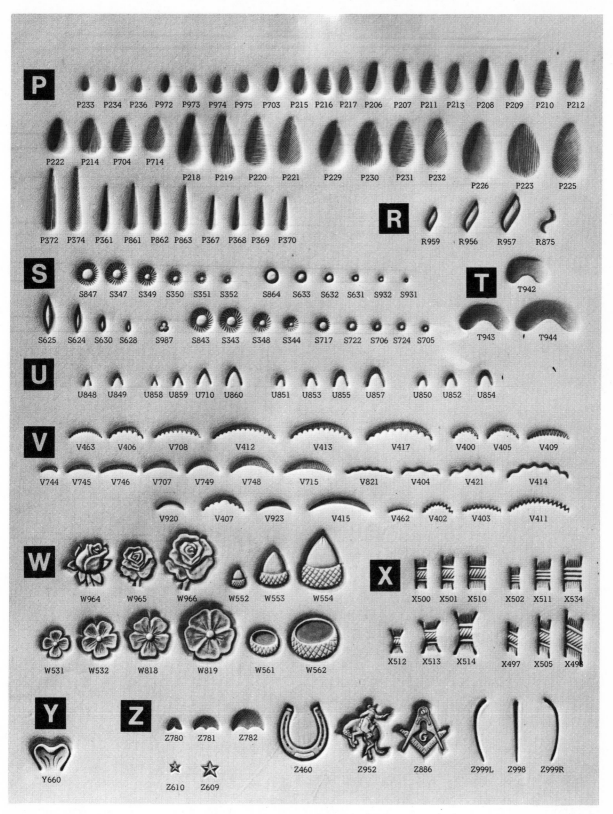

Fig. 4-3. More stamping tool impressions.
(The Craftool Company)

pear shaders because they usually result in a darker shaded area and a greater contrast of textures.

BEVELERS

The working surface of the beveler is tapered toward the back and is rounded slightly across the width. The taper causes it to be thicker at the front than at the back. The beveler may be purchased with a smooth burnishing surface or with a textured surface, and in a variety of sizes, as shown in Fig. 4-2.

This stamp is used to bevel down one side of the swivel knife cut, giving your design a three-dimensional effect. See Fig. 4-13. Beveling the design will make it stand out in bold relief. The less prominent parts of your design are stamped down to make them appear subdued. The small size bevelers are useful in beveling around sharp, curved cuts, and the large sizes in beveling along straight cuts. The bevelers help to bring out a contrasting rich brown in your designs.

STOP TOOLS

The working end of the stop stamp is small and is shaped like a wedge. It comes in several sizes and with both smooth and textured burnishing surfaces. Fig. 4-2.

The stop stamp is used to beautify the end cuts in flowers, stems, and leaves. Note Fig. 4-17.

BACKGROUND TOOLS

Background tools (Fig. 4-2) are available in a variety of sizes, shapes and textures.

Background tools are used to stamp down leather around your design to the depth of the swivel cuts. Fig. 4-18. Backgrounding increases the three-dimensional effect of your design and helps to add a contrasting rich brown color. The tools with small working surfaces are useful to background in close areas. The larger tools result in a minimum of stretching and seldom cut through the leather.

USING TWO GUSSETS

Gussets are extra pieces of leather used to form the sides of numerous leather articles. They are especially

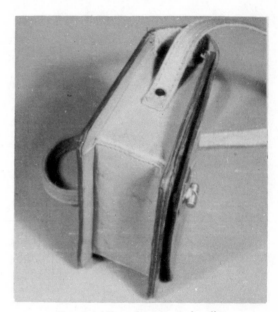

Fig. 4-4. Use of gusset in handbag.

useful in purses and handbags. Fig. 4-4. The gussets fold flat when a purse or handbag is closed, making the project compact. When the purse or handbag is opened, the gussets unfold, making the contents easily accessible.

FILIGREE

Filigree is a method of ornamenting carved-leather designs. Filigree is done by cutting through the leather in the

*Fig. 4-5. Design suggestions. Numbers identify
stamping tools used. (Craftool Company)*

background area of a design with a swivel knife. The leather cut from the background can then be removed, forming windows or openings in the design. Lining material, usually of a contrasting color, is cemented to the flesh side of the leather and is visible through the windows. Special filigree blades are available for most swivel knives.

Filigree is popular with many leather-crafters because it provides deep, three-dimensional effect and contrast of color in design backgrounds.

VEINING TOOLS

The veiner has convex and concave edges and is shaped like a crescent. It is available in a variety of textures and sizes. Shell tools and barkers are some-times substituted for veiners. See Fig. 4-2.

The veiner is used to form veins along the center ribs of large leaves and to rep-resent folds in flower petals. Fig. 4-14. You may also use it as a stop stamp for end cuts.

SEEDER TOOLS

The working surface of the seeder is concave resulting in a dome-shaped im-pression. It is available in several sizes. Fig. 4-3. The seeder is used to make seeds in flower centers and fern swirls.

MULEFOOT TOOLS

The mulefoot stamp is "U" or "V"-shaped. The mulefoot is available in several sizes and textures. See Fig. 4-3.

You will find the mulefoot stamp use-ful in decorating leaf and flower stems, and in front of stop cuts. Fig. 4-16.

BILLFOLD, FRAME KEY CASE, KNIFE CASE, BELT, BOOK ENDS, LETTER HOLDER
(Projects, Unit 4)

We will now explore deeper into the enchanting art of leather carving. In Unit 3 we gained experience in carving thin leather with a swivel knife. By carv-ing into thicker leather used in Unit 4 projects, we can see the deep alluring effects made with stamping tools, as our design is carved and stamped deep into the leather.

The projects presented in this unit are small and inexpensive, yet useful and attractive. Try to think of other projects which you can make by following the general outline of processes presented in this unit. Perhaps you will want to make larger and more expensive projects than those presented in this unit, such as note books, handbags, picture album, scrap

books, gun cases, and camera cases. The procedures described here are applicable to many different projects.

TOOLS REQUIRED

Pencil, skiving knife, skife, scissors, small sponge or cloth, spoon and tracer modeling tool, swivel knife, straight edge, edge beveler, edge creaser, embossing wheel and carriage, dividers, one and four prong thonging chisels, mallet, re-volving spring punch, snap button set, fid, lacing needle, gouge, and stamping tools.

MATERIALS REQUIRED

Tooling Calfskin and Carving Cowhide.

In making piece A, the leather you will

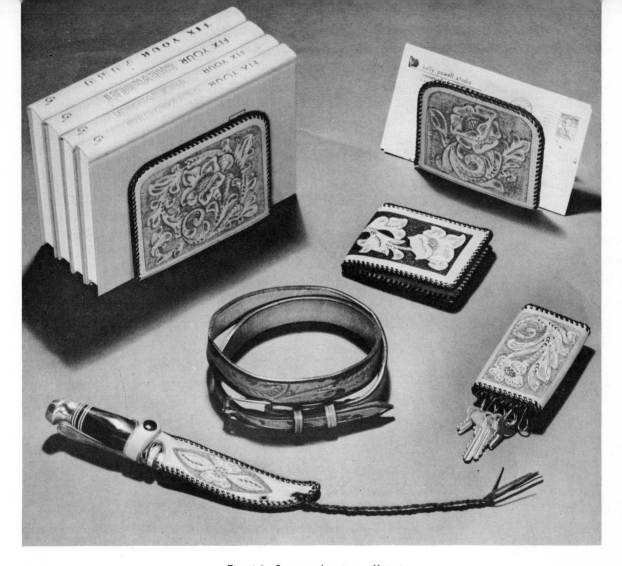

Fig. 4-6. Suggested projects, Unit 4.

carve, except for a belt, should be approximately 4/5 oz. weight carving cowhide. If you choose to make a belt, the leather should be 8/9 oz. weight.

Leather pieces B and C of the billfold and pieces C and D of the frame key case should be 1-1/2 oz. Great strength is not important for these pieces. Thin leather will make the project less bulky.

Tracing paper, rubber cement, lacing, thread.

On a number of projects, you will need a strong thread such as is used by shoe cobblers to sew inside pockets. Thread made of linen, nylon, or silk will work well with leathercraft projects. Before

using thread, you should rub it with a piece of paraffin or beeswax to lubricate and waterproof it.

ACCESSORIES

SNAP BUTTON.

KEY FRAME. A metal frame with 4 to 6 hooks to hold keys. Key frames are held firmly to leather with eyelets or rivets.

EYELET. A hollow cylinder of metal with a flange on one end. It may be used to fasten metal key frames to leather or to prevent a knife from cutting its leather case.

RIVET. It is made of two parts: a button and an eyelet. The parts may be fastened together with a snap button set. Rivets may be used to fasten metal key frames to leather, or to prevent a knife from cutting its leather case.

Fig. 4-7. Completed billfold.

FINISHES

Diluted oxalic acid. (Described in Unit 1).

Leather dressing.

Wax.

Dyes. Dyes produce interesting effects when used on design backgrounds. Dyes may be applied with a small camel hair brush. Many colors are available. Specially prepared aniline dyes are water proof. India ink may also be used to color backgrounds.

PROJECT ANALYSIS

From the analysis chart, page 7, you can quickly determine processes required in making Unit 4 projects. Select a project that you would like to make for this unit. Or, you may wish to design a project of your own requiring similar processes.

PROCEDURES FOR MAKING BILL-FOLDS, FRAME KEY CASES, BELTS, BOOK ENDS AND LETTER HOLDERS

The illustrations which follow show the making of the billfold shown in Fig. 4-7.

The directions for making other projects in this unit are nearly identical.

BILLFOLD

Procedure:
1. Make the templates. Figs. 4-8, 4-9, 4-10 (Step 1, Unit 1).
2. Transfer the templates to leather (Step 2, Unit 1).
3. Cut leather with a skiving knife and straight edge (Step 3, Unit 2).
4. Cut leather with scissors (Step 3, Unit 1).
5. Prepare your design (Step 5, Unit 2).
6. Condition the leather (Step 5, Unit 1).
7. Transfer your design to leather (Step 7, Unit 2).
8. Incise your design with a swivel knife (Step 8, Unit 3).
9. Decorate your design with saddle stamps.
    You should always use a marble slab or a similar smooth, hard-surfaced piece of material to protect your bench top when using stamping tools. It is advisable to practice and experiment with each stamp on a piece of scrap leather of the same kind and thickness as the leather you are using for your project. Your practice will help you get the knack of using the tool and develop con-

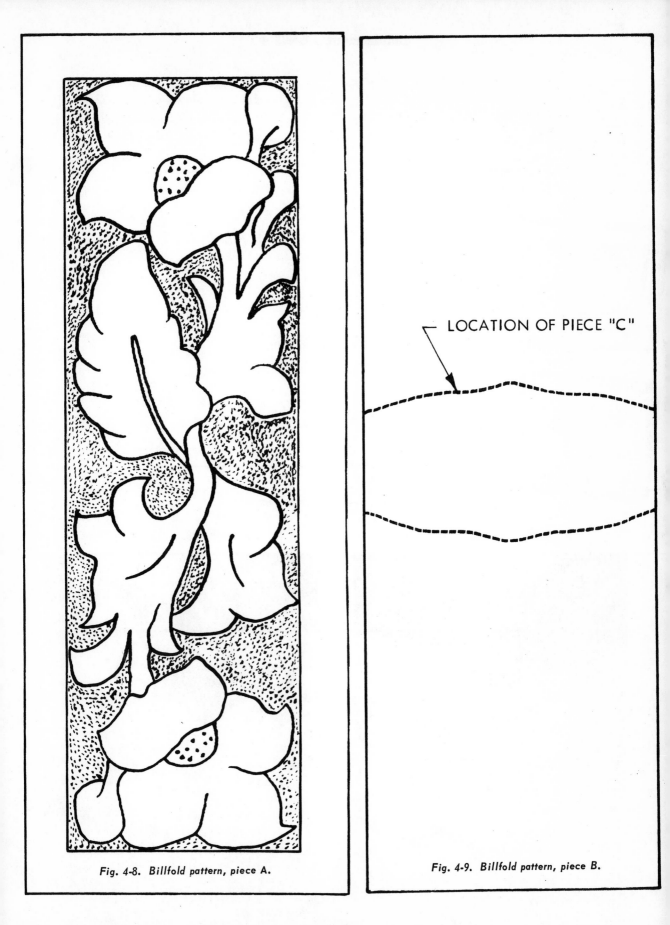

LOCATION OF PIECE "C"

Fig. 4-8. Billfold pattern, piece A.

Fig. 4-9. Billfold pattern, piece B.

fidence in your work. You will also learn to properly condition leather for decoration with the various saddle stamps.

a. Camouflage your design
   (1) Hold the shank of the camouflage tool between your thumb, index, and second finger in a vertical

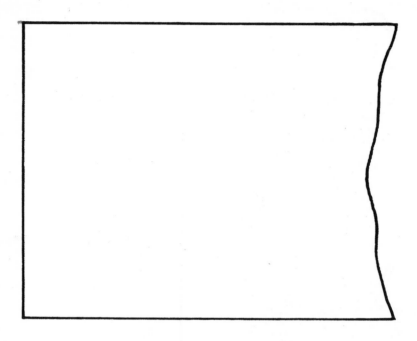

Fig. 4-10. Billfold pattern, piece C.

Fig. 4-11. Camouflaging the design.

Fig. 4-12. Using shading tool.

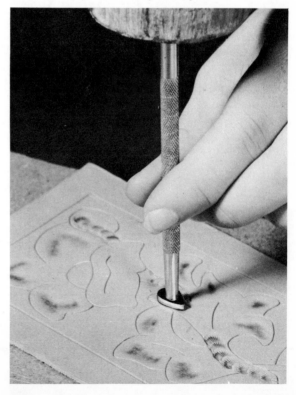

position. Rest your little finger on the surface of the leather for support.

(2) Begin at the bottom of a stem, leaf, or fern swirl with its concave edge facing downward. Strike the stamp firmly with a mallet. Fig. 4-11.

(3) Lift the stamp, place it above the impression previously made and strike it again with the mallet.

(4) Proceed toward the top of the stem, leaf, or fern swirl using uniform spacing. Lean the tool slightly to one side for fern swirls. Gradually lighten the tap of the mallet as you progress upward.

b. Shade your design

(1) Hold the pear shader as you did the camouflage tool.

(2) Begin near the edge of a leaf or flower petal. Tip the stamp slightly to one side and strike it firmly with a mallet. Fig. 4-12. Your fingers should act as springs causing the tool to rebound to its beginning position.

(3) Using a rolling action with your wrist, move the stamp to a new position toward the inside of the leaf or flower petal. Strike the stamp again with the mallet.

(4) As you proceed inward with succeeding taps, gradually decrease the pressure on the mallet to form a dish-shaped impression. The distance between the shaded area and the swivel cuts should be 1/16 to 1/8 in.

c. Bevel your design

(1) Hold the beveler as you did the camouflage tool.

(2) Select a leaf segment or flower petal that you wish to appear behind or under its adjacent segment or flower petal. Place the toe, thick portion, of the beveler in the swivel knife cut on its outside edge. Strike the beveler firmly with a mallet. Fig. 4-13.

(3) Move the beveler along the cut, about one fourth the distance of its width, and strike it again with the mallet.

(4) As you approach the end of the cut with succeeding taps, decrease the pressure on the mallet to taper the bevel. If the beveled area is bumpy, you probably moved the beveler too far with each tap or failed to hold it vertical. Rough places can usually be smoothed by going over them again.

Fig. 4-13. Beveling the design.

(5) Study your design carefully. Always bevel away from the parts of your design that you wish to become prominent.

d. Vein your design

(1) Hold the veiner as you did the camouflage tool.

(2) Begin near the bottom of a large leaf. Place one side of the

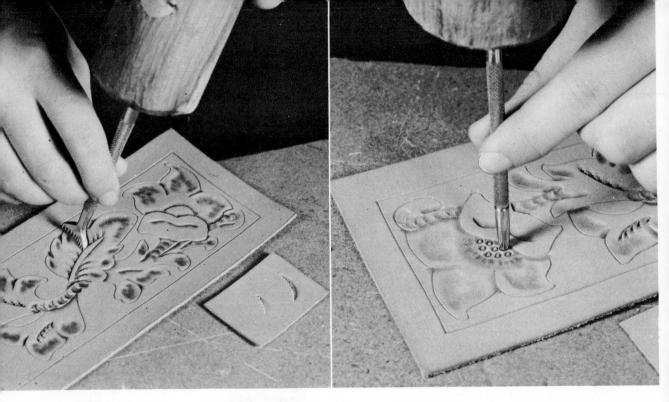

Fig. 4-14. Left. Veining the design. Fig. 4-15. Right.
Decorating flower centers with seeder stamping tool.

veiner next to the center rib of the leaf with its concave edge facing downward. Tip the veiner about 30 degrees toward the leaf rib and strike it firmly with a mallet. Fig. 4-14.

(3) Lift the stamp, place it above the impression previously made and strike it again with the mallet.

(4) Proceed toward the top of the leaf rib using uniform spacing.

e. Decorate the flower centers in your design

(1) Stamp lines around the flower centers of your design to represent rays. Use a textured pear shader held at an angle of about 30 deg.

(2) Hold the seeder as you did the camouflage tool. The moisture content of your leather should be low.

(3) Place the seeder near the outside edge of a flower center. Tip the stamp away from the flower center at an angle of about 15 deg. and strike it lightly several times with a mallet. Fig. 4-15.

This will give the flower center a rounded appearance. If the impression is flat on top, it is an indication that you need to use more pressure on the stamp. Be careful not to pierce through the leather.

(4) Move the stamp to a new position around the outside edge of the flower center and strike it again with several light blows of the mallet. The seed impressions should barely touch each other but should not overlap.

(5) Continue around the outside edge of the flower center using uniform spacing.

(6) Hold the stamp in a vertical position and stamp the remaining seed impressions on the flower center.

f. Decorate your design with a mulefoot tool

(1) Hold the mulefoot as you did the camouflage tool. The moisture content of your leather should be low. Only one to three impressions are usually made in

72

one location.

(2) Place the mulefoot in front of an end cut with its concave edge facing downward. Lean the stamp away from the end cut at an angle of about 15 deg. and strike it lightly several times with a mallet. Be careful not to cut through the leather. Fig. 4-16.

(3) Lift the stamp, place it above the impression previously made and strike it again with several light blows of the mallet. The second impression should be of less

Fig. 4-17. *Decorating design with a stop tool.*

tent of your leather should be low.

(2) Place the stop in one of the end cuts of your design. Lean the stamp forward at an angle of about 45 deg. and strike it firm-

Fig. 4-18. *Backgrounding the design.*

Fig. 4-16. *Decorating design with a mulefoot tool.*

depth than the first.

(4) Continue with one or more impressions of less depth and using uniform spacing.

g. Decorate your design with a stop tool.

(1) Hold the stop as you did the camouflage. The moisture con-

ly with a mallet. Be careful not to cut through your leather. Fig. 4-17.

(3) Stamp the remaining end cuts of your design in the same way.

h. Background your design.

(1) Hold the background tool as you did the camouflage tool. The moisture content of your leather

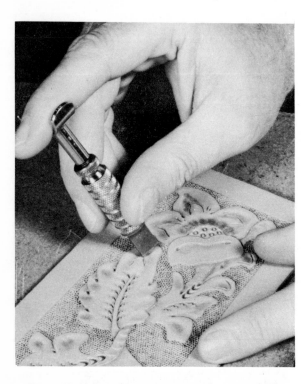

Fig. 4-19. Making decorative cuts with carving knife.

should be low for tools with small working surfaces such as number 101 and medium for tools with larger working surfaces, such as number 888. Fig. 4-18.

(2) Begin next to the edge of your design with a wedge-shaped or half-round tool held in a vertical position. Place the broad side of the tool next to the design with with its working surface just above the leather. Strike the stamp firmly with a mallet. See Fig. 4-18. Your fingers should act as springs causing the tool

to rebound to its beginning position.

(3) Move the tool to a new position around the edge of your design and strike it again with the mallet. The impressions should barely touch each other.

(4) Continue around the design using uniform taps with the mallet.

(5) Fill in the background area between your design and its border with a round or rectangular-shaped tool.

(6) Try to prevent:

(a) Stamping into your design or its border.

(b) Uneven background areas.

(c) Overlapping the stamp impressions.

(d) Piercing your leather.

Fig. 4-20. Marking the edge to be stitched.

10. Make the decorative cuts.

Decorative cuts should follow the contour of flowers, leaves, and stems.

a. Lightly dampen the surface of your leather with a sponge or cloth. Strop the swivel knife blade on a rouge board.

b. Hold the swivel knife as you did to incise your design.

c. Begin near the tip of a flower petal or leaf segment. Turn the knife with your fingers so that the broad side of its blade is parallel with your body. Start the cut with a heavy downward pressure and turn the knife sharply with your fingers as you draw it toward the flower or leaf center. Gradually release pressure on the knife as you make the turn. Lift the blade from the leather, ending the cut with a fine line. Fig. 4-19.

d. Make smaller cuts on each side of the main cut slanting them inward.

e. Continue with the remaining decorative cuts in the same way.

11. Edge bevel piece C. (Step 4, Unit 1).

12. Edge crease piece C. (Step 6, Unit 1).

13. Emboss piece C. (Step 13, Unit 3).

14. Skive. (Step 10, Unit 2).

15. Cut a groove to make a fold. (Step 15, Unit 3).

16. Attach skiver lining. (Step 16, Unit 3).

17. Trim a skiver lining. (Step 17, Unit 3).

18. Stitch with thread.

a. Assemble parts B and C.

  (1) Cement the edges. (Step 11, Unit 2).

  (2) Press the cemented edges of piece C to piece B.

b. Mark the edge to be stitched with a double line marking tool or a pair of dividers. The mark should be about 1/8 in. from the edge of the leather. Fig. 4-20.

c. Space the stitches.

Using a spacing wheel, follow closely the line you made in step b. A spacing wheel makes small equidistant dents in the leather. Fig. 4-21.

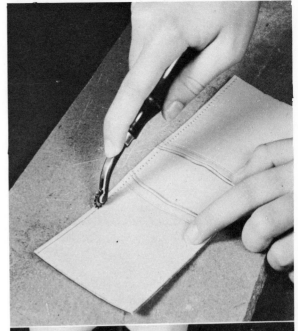

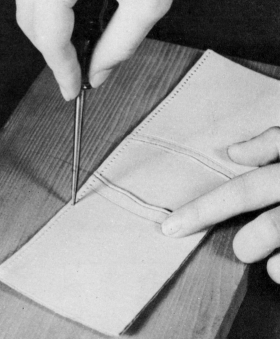

Fig. 4-21. Above. Using spacing wheel to mark stitching spaces. Fig. 4-22. Below. Punching holes for stitches.

d. Punch holes for stitches.

Using an awl, punch holes through the leather at the places you marked with a spacing wheel in step c. Fig. 4-22.

e. Begin at one end (either end) with

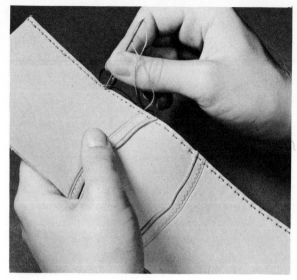

Fig. 4-23. Left. Stitching through all holes with strong thread.
Fig. 4-24. Right. Stitching to the beginning stitch.

a threaded harness needle, stitching through each hole to the other end. Fig. 4-23.

f. Sew back across the leather, using thread to fill alternate spaces. Fig. 4-24.

g. Tie the beginning and ending pieces of thread together, fastening them securely to the edge of the leather. Lace will cover the thread knot.

19. Assemble the leather parts.

Cement piece B to piece A. Note that piece B is about 3/16 in. shorter than piece A. This is to help prevent wrinkles in your bill-fold when you fold it. Fig. 4-25.

20. Thong. (Step 13, Unit 2).

21. Lace with a double button hole stitch. (Step 22, Unit 3).

22. Dye the background of your design. Use #2 camel's hair brush.

a. Dip brush in a bottle of prepared dye. Wipe excess dye from the brush on the inside edge of the bottle.

b. Place the point of the brush next to your design and pull it toward you, following the outline of your design

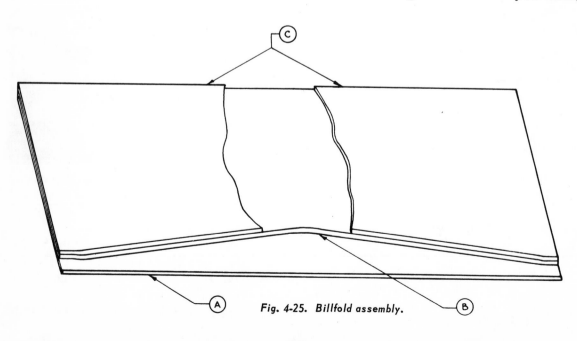

Fig. 4-25. Billfold assembly.

carefully. Dye a small area of the background at a time. Fill in the background space between your de-

Fig. 4-26. Dye the background of your design.

sign and its border before you move to another area, Fig. 4-26.

23. Apply a finish. (Step 8, Unit 1)

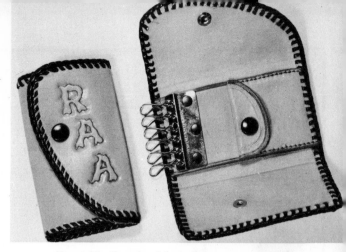

Fig. 4-27. Completed frame key case.

FRAME KEY CASE

Refer to project #1, if necessary, for an explanation of the procedures.

Procedure:
1. Make the templates, Figs. 4-28, 4-29, 4-30, 4-31.
2. Transfer the templates to leather.
3. Cut leather with a skiving knife and straight edge.
4. Cut leather with scissors.
5. Prepare your design.
6. Condition the leather.

Fig. 4-28. Frame key case pattern, piece A.

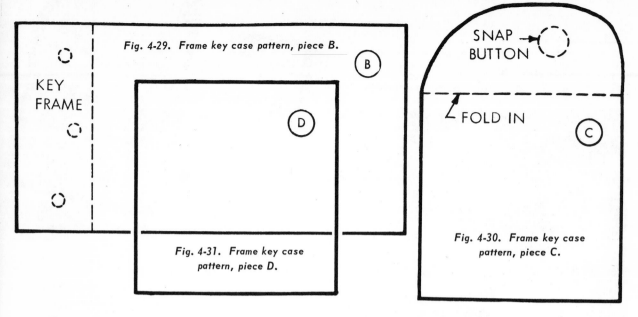

Fig. 4-29. Frame key case pattern, piece B.

KEY FRAME

Fig. 4-31. Frame key case pattern, piece D.

SNAP BUTTON

FOLD IN

Fig. 4-30. Frame key case pattern, piece C.

7. Transfer your design to leather.
8. Incise your design with a swivel knife.
9. Decorate your design with saddle stamps.
10. Make the decorative cuts.
11. Edge bevel pieces B and C.
12. Edge crease pieces B and C.
13. Emboss pieces B and C.

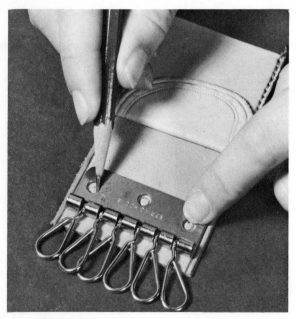

Fig. 4-32. Marking through holes of key frame.

14. Skive.
15. Cut grooves to make the folds.
16. Attach a skiver lining.
17. Trim a skiver lining.
18. Stitch with thread.

19. Fasten the key frame.
   a. Prepare leather to receive the key frame.
      (1) Place the key frame in the de-

Fig. 4-33. Punching holes with revolving spring punch.

sired position and mark through the holes of the key frame onto the leather with a pencil. Fig. 4-32.
      (2) Remove the key frame from the leather.
      (3) Punch holes through the leather with a revolving spring punch where you made the pencil marks. Fig. 4-33.

   If you plan to use rivets to attach the key frame, punch #2 holes. Punch size 5 holes if you plan to use eyelets to attach the key frame.
   b. Set rivets or eyelets.
      You can use either rivets or

78

eyelets to fasten your key frame to leather.

(1) Set rivets. Fig. 4-34.

   (a) Locate the key over the #2 holes on the grain side of the leather.

   (b) Push the eyelets through the #2 holes from the flesh side of the leather.

   (c) Position the eyelets over the stud and eyelet anvil of the snap button set.

   (d) Place the caps over the eyelets.

   (e) Insert the concave end of the snap button set over the caps and set the rivets with a wood mallet.

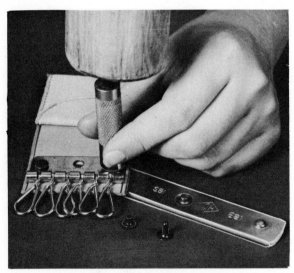

Fig. 4-34. Setting rivets.

(2) Set eyelets. Fig. 4-35.

   (a) Locate the key frame over the number #5 holes on the grain side of the leather.

   (b) Push the eyelets into the #5 holes from the flesh side of the leather. The flanges on the eyelets will remain on the flesh side of the leather.

   (c) Place the eyelets onto a metal base.

   (d) Insert the point of an eyelet

setter into the hole of the eyelet and set the eyelets with a wood mallet.

20. Assemble the leather parts.

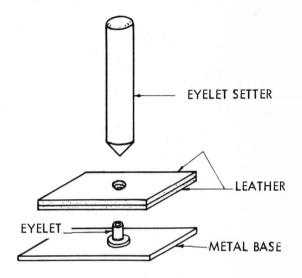

Fig. 4-35. Setting eyelets.

21. Thong.
22. Lace with a double button hole stitch.
23. Attach a snap button (Step 7, Unit 1).
24. Dye the background of your design.
25. Apply a finish.

KNIFE CASE

Refer to project #1, if not otherwise indicated, for an explanation of the procedures listed below.

Procedure:

1. Make the templates. Figs. 4-37, 4-38, and 4-39.
2. Transfer the templates to leather.
3. Cut leather with a skiving knife and straight edge.
4. Cut leather with scissors.
5. Prepare your design.
6. Condition the leather.
7. Transfer your design to leather.
8. Incise your design with a swivel knife.

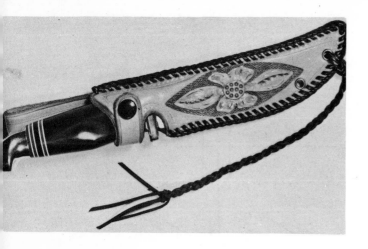

Fig. 4-36. Completed knife case.

9. Decorate your design with saddle stamps.
10. Make the decorative cuts.
11. Edge bevel.
12. Edge crease.
13. Emboss.
14. Skive.
15. Stitch with thead.
    a. Cement piece C to piece A.
    b. Fold down the upper strap of piece A and cement it to piece C.
    c. Stitch the cemented edges together.
16. Assemble the leather parts.
17. Thong.
18. Attach a snap button.
19. Lace with a double button hole stitch.
20. Set rivets or eyelets.
    a. Punch holes through leather case with revolving spring punch next to the edge which will receive cutting edge of your knife.
    b. Insert rivets or eyelets through the holes and set them (Step 19, Unit 2).
21. Dye the background of your design.
22. Apply finish.

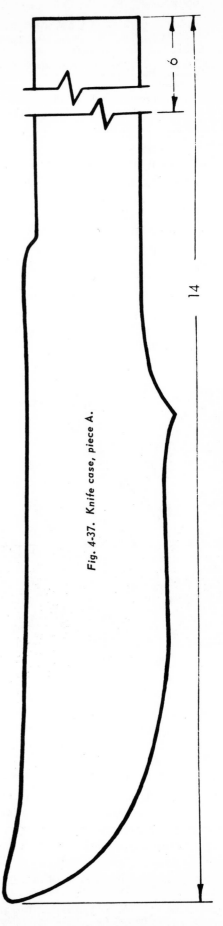

Fig. 4-37. Knife case, piece A.

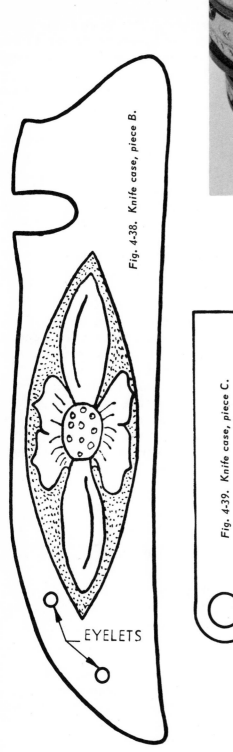

Fig. 4-38. Knife case, piece B.

EYELETS

Fig. 4-39. Knife case, piece C.

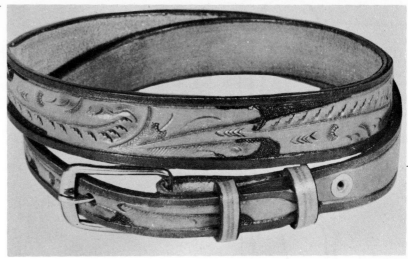

Fig. 4-40. Completed belt.

BELT

Refer to project #1, if not otherwise indicated, for an explanation of the procedure listed below.

Procedure:
1. Make the templates. Figs. 4-41 and 4-42.

    Measure around your waist with a flexible tape. Add 10 in. to this measurement for your A template length.
2. Transfer the templates to leather.
3. Cut leather with a skiving knife and straight edge.
4. Cut leather with scissors.
5. Condition the leather.
6. Edge bevel.
7. Edge crease.
8. Prepare your design.
9. Transfer your design to leather.
10. Incise your design with a swivel knife.
11. Decorate your design with saddle stamps.
12. Make the decorative cuts.

13. Assemble piece B, your belt keeper.
    a. Skive 1/2 in. distance from each end. Skive one end on flesh side and the other end on grain side.
    b. Cement the skived ends.
    c. Stitch the keeper with strong thread.

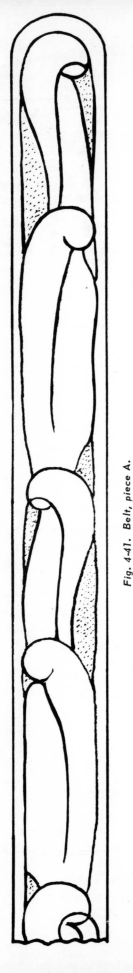

Fig. 4-41. Belt, piece A.

Fig. 4-42. Belt keeper pattern, piece B.

14. Fasten the buckle.
   a. Fold a flap 4 in. long from the square end of piece A. Mark a line about 3/4 in. long perpendicular to the fold and in the center of the width of piece A.
   b. Unfold the flap and punch a #4 hole at each end of the line you marked in step a.
   c. Cut a 1/8 in. wide slit between the the holes you punched in step b.
   d. Assemble the buckle through the slit you made in step c.
   e. Attach the flap with two or more snap buttons spaced about one inch apart.
   f. Fasten your belt keeper between two of the snap buttons you assembled in step e.
15. Fit your belt to your waist.
   a. Place your belt around your waist, pull it to a snug fit and use a pencil to mark the leather where a hole is to be punched.
   b. Punch a #3 hole in the location you marked in step a.
   c. Punch two or more additional holes spaced about 3/4 in. apart.
16. Dye the background of your design.
17. Apply a finish.

BOOKENDS

Refer to project #1, if not otherwise indicated, for an explanation of the procedure listed below.

Procedure:
1. Make the template. Fig. 4-44.
2. Transfer the templates to leather.
3. Cut leather with a skiving knife and straight edge.
4. Cut leather with scissors.
5. Prepare your design.
6. Condition the leather.
7. Transfer your design to leather.
8. Incise your design with a swivel knife.

Fig. 4-43. Completed bookends.

Fig. 4-44. Bookend cover pattern.

LEATHER
COVERING

METAL BASE

$4\frac{1}{4}$

$5\frac{1}{4}$

$6\frac{3}{4}$

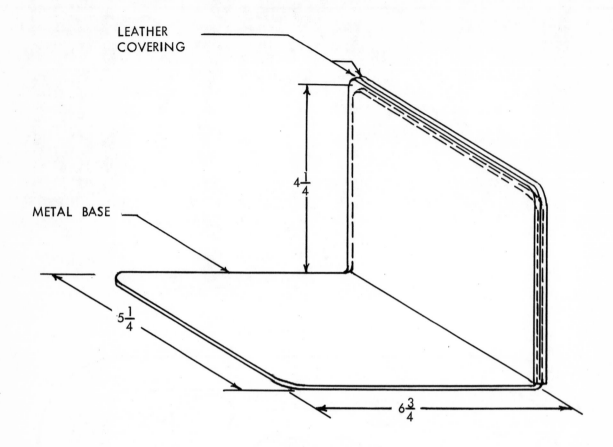

Fig. 4-45. Assembling bookends.

9. Decorate your design with saddle stamps.
10. Make the decorative cuts.
11. Edge bevel.
12. Edge crease.
13. Skive.
14. Assemble the leather parts.
15. Thong.
16. Lace with a double buttonhole stitch.
17. Dye the background of your design.
18. Apply a finish.
19. Prepare the metal bases for your bookends. Fig. 4-45.
    a. Cut two pieces of 16 ga. metal 5-1/4 in. wide and 11 in. long.
    b. Bend a 4-1/4 right angle in the length of each piece of metal.
    c. Insert the metal bases into your finished leather coverings.

LETTER HOLDER

Refer to project #1, if not otherwise indicated, for an explanation of the procedure given below.

Procedure:
1. Make the template. Fig. 4-47.
2. Transfer the templates to leather.
3. Cut leather with a skiving knife and straight edge.
4. Cut leather with scissors.
5. Prepare your design.
6. Condition the leather.
7. Transfer your design to leather.
8. Incise your design with a swivel knife.
9. Decorate your design with saddle stamps.

Fig. 4-46. Completed letter holder.

Fig. 4-47. Letter holder cover pattern.

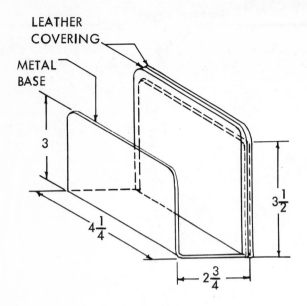

LEATHER
COVERING

METAL
BASE

3

4 1/4

2 3/4

3 1/2

Fig. 4-48. Assembling letter holder.

10. Make the decorative cuts.
11. Edge bevel.
12. Edge crease.
13. Skive.
14. Assemble the leather parts.
15. Thong.
16. Lace with a double button hole stitch.
17. Dye the background of your design.
18. Apply a finish.
19. Prepare the metal base for your letter holder. Fig. 4-48.
   a. Cut a piece of 16 ga. metal 4-1/4 in. x 9-1/4 in.
   b. Bend at right angle 3-1/2 in. from one end.
   c. Bend at right angle 3 in. from the other end.
   d. Insert the metal base into finished leather covering.

QUIZ - UNIT 4

1. We need a vegetable tanned leather to decorate designs with stamping tools. True or false?

2. A ruffled appearance representing veins and folds is usually made with a pear shader. True or false?

3. Lining material is seldom used with filigree designs. True or false?

4. One of the stamping tools we use to decorate leather has a convex and a concave edge. It is shaped like a crescent with evenly spaced lines running from the inside of the crescent to its outside. Its name is camouflage; pear shader; beveler; mulefoot.

5. To make bowl-shaped impressions in flower petals and leaves, giving them a three-dimensional effect, we need the beveler; camouflage; veiner; pear shader.

6. A U or V-shaped tool we use to decorate leaf and flower petal stems is called a veiner; camouflage; mulefoot; gusset.

7. One of the saddle stamps is shaped like a wedge and is used to decorate end cuts. It is usually called the camouflage; stop; mulefoot; filigree.

8. The tool we need to stamp down the leather around our design is called the pear shader; background; veiner.

9. How can you accomplish a filigree design?

10. For what purpose would you use a gusset in a project?

Fig. 4-49. Alternate designs for Unit 4.

Billfold design suggestions.

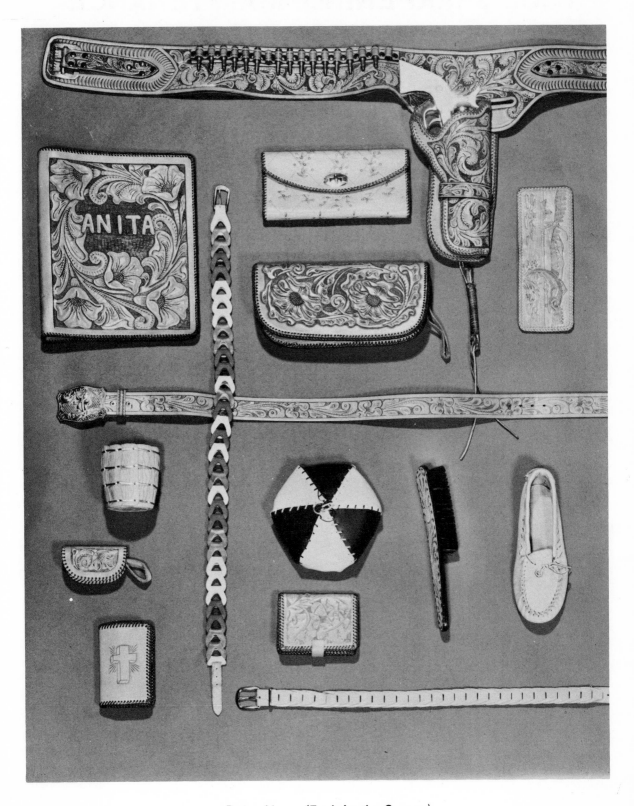

Project Ideas.   (Tandy Leather Company)

TOOL SHARPENING, MAINTENANCE

1. How to sharpen scissors, shears, knives, chisels, modeling tools, revolving spring punches.
2. Tool and material storage.

Sharp, clean tools will help you work more efficiently and safely.

Oil, applied sparingly to all moving parts, will help tools function easily and last longer.

SCISSORS AND SHEARS. To sharpen scissors and shears, hold the blade firmly against a sharpening stone. Pull the cutting edge across the stone, being careful to maintain the angle to which the shears were originally sharpened by the manufacturer. See Fig. 5-1.

SKIVING KNIFE. For best results, check this tool for sharpness before you

Fig. 5-1. How to sharpen scissors and shears.

use it. You can do this by touching the cutting edge lightly against your thumb nail. Slight pressure will cause a sharp

knife to make a small cut in your thumb nail without injury. If the blade needs sharpening, hold the cutting edge firmly against a sharpening stone at the angle established by the manufacturer. Pull the blade across the sharpening stone toward the cutting edge. Use several strokes if necessary. Sharpen the other

Fig. 5-2. Sharpening skiving knife.

side of the blade in the same way, Fig. 5-2.

MODELING TOOLS. Small nicks or burrs may be removed by polishing with a fine grit abrasive paper.

EDGE BEVELER. You can sharpen the cutting edge of this tool with a small jeweler's file, Fig. 5-3.

REVOLVING SPRING PUNCH. This

tool requires but little care if it is used correctly. To sharpen this tool, you can use a narrow strip of fine grit abrasive paper in the same way you use a cloth to

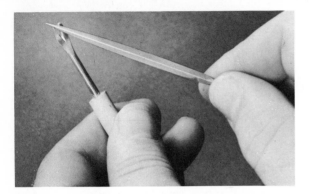

Fig. 5-3. Sharpening an edge beveler.

buff your shoes. Always sharpen the outside of the tube, Fig. 5-4.

The anvil may be reconditioned by smoothing it with a flat mill file.

THONGING CHISEL. To sharpen this tool, place the broad side of the chisel

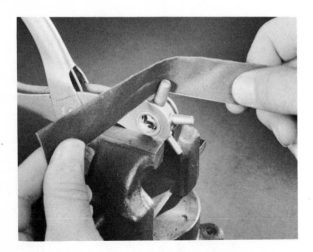

Fig. 5-4. Sharpening a revolving spring punch.

firmly against a sharpening stone. Push the chisel in the direction of the cutting edges. Sharpen both sides of the prongs, Fig. 5-6.

SWIVEL KNIFE. You may find that the blade needs additional sharpening before you can use it satisfactorily. To sharpen the blade, hone both edges on a fine sharpening stone. Hold the blade firmly

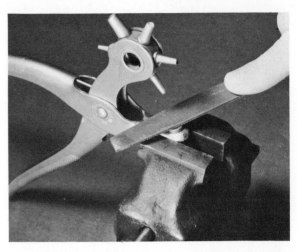

Fig. 5-5. Smoothing the anvil of a revolving spring punch.

against the surface of the sharpening stone and push it across in a forward direction. Be careful to hold the blade at the angle to which it was originally ground. Fig. 5-7.

Fig. 5-6. Sharpening a thonging chisel.

You can polish the sharpened edges to a high gloss by pulling them over a leather

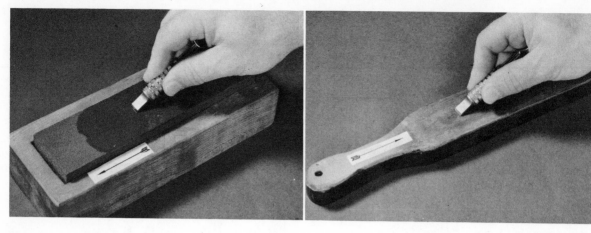

Fig. 5-7. *Sharpening a swivel knife.*   Fig. 5-8. *Polishing a swivel knife blade.*

strop saturated with a mixture of jewelers' rouge and neatsfoot oil. To polish the blade, hold the sharpened edge firmly against the leather strop. Pull the blade across the strop away from its cutting edge. A strop may be prepared by tacking a piece of cowhide, grain side up, on a piece of scrap wood. The strop can then be rubbed with neatsfoot oil followed with jewelers' rouge. Careful polishing will help prevent dragging as you make cuts in the leather. Keep the strop handy for further use, Fig. 5-8.

Tool and Material Storage

A tool panel or cabinet is a convenient way to store tools as part of efficient and safe shop management, Fig. 5-9. Small accessories with multiple parts, such as snaps and key posts, may be easily stored in labeled containers. Hides and skins can be sorted into the various kinds, rolled tightly with utility paper, labeled and then stored where they can be kept dry and away from direct sunlight. Special jars for storing finishes and cements are available from leather supply companies.

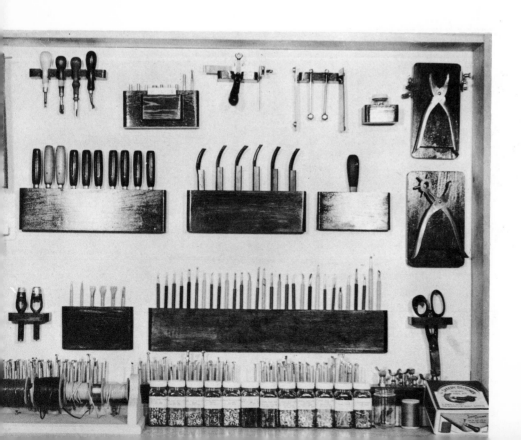

Fig. 5-9. *Typical leather tool cabinet.*

REFERENCES

Baird, F. O., Leather Secrets. Manitou Springs, Colorado: F. O. Baird, Publisher.

Cherry, Raymond, General Leathercraft. Bloomington, Illinois: McKnight & McKnight Publishing Company.

Griffin, Ken, The Art of Leather Carving. Los Angeles, California: Craftool Co.

Groneman, Chris H., Leatherwork. Peoria, Illinois: Chas. A. Bennett Company, Inc.

Ohio Leather Company, The Story of Leather. Girard, Ohio: The Ohio Leather Company.

Shelton, Al, Operation, Leather Carving. Los Angeles, California: Craftool Company.

Smith, Joey, The New Craftool Bag. Los Angeles, California: Craftool Company.

Smith, Lavon, The Fundamentals of Leather Carving. Houston, Texas: Tandy Leather Company.

Tanner's Council of America, Inc., Dictionary of Leather Terminology, New York City, New York: Tanner's Council of America.

ACKNOWLEDGMENTS

This is to express my gratitude to the many individuals, leather industries, and leather supply companies for their interest and cooperation in the development of this text. Special acknowledgment is due the following:

My wife, Lois, for her help in the construction of projects and for her patience and encouragement.

James H. Jacobsen, for preparing many of the inked tracings of drawings used in this text.

Dr. Dempsey E. Reid, Dr. Herman Griesenbrock and other colleagues of Western, for their suggestions and cooperation.

Leather Industries of America, New York City, New York.

Longhorn Leather Co., Dallas, Texas.

Ohio Leather Company, Girard, Ohio.

Tandy Leather Co., Fort Worth, Texas.

Fred W. Zimmerman

INDEX

CRANES
DUMP TRUCKS
BULLDOZERS

AND OTHER
BUILDING
MACHINES

TERRY JENNINGS

Kingfisher Books

NEW YORK

KINGFISHER BOOKS
Grisewood & Dempsey Inc.
95 Madison Avenue
New York, New York 10016

First American edition 1993
2 4 6 8 10 9 7 5 3
Copyright © Grisewood & Dempsey Ltd. 1992

Library of Congress Cataloging-in-Publication Data
Jennings, Terry J.
Cranes, dump trucks, bulldozers & other building machines
Terry Jennings. — 1st American ed.
p.cm. (How things work) Includes index.
Summary: Investigates, in text and labelled diagrams and
illustrations, the functions of various kinds of building machines
and how they work. Includes instructions for related projects
and experiments
1. Construction equipment—Juvenile literature.
[1. Construction equipment. 2. Machinery.]
I. Title. II. Series: How things work.
TH900.J46 1993
690-dc20 92-23370 CIP AC

ISBN 1-85697-866-4 (lib. bdg.)
ISBN 1-85697-865-6 (pbk.)

Printed in Hong Kong

Series editor: Jackie Gaff
Series designer: David West Children's Books
Author: Terry Jennings
Text contributors: Jacqui Bailey, Jackie Gaff, Chris Maynard
Consultant: Robert C. McWilliam (The Science Museum)
Cover illustration: Micheal Fisher (Garden Studio)
Illustrators: Darren Fletcher pp. 32-3; Chris Forsey pp. 6-7,
(insets 10-11), 16-21, 38-9; Hayward Art Group pp. 10-11,
14-15, 28-9; Simon Tegg pp. 8-9, 12-13, 22-7, 36-7;
Ian Thompson pp. 2-5, 30-1, 34-5.
Research: A.R. Blann

The publishers would like to thank: Benford Construction
Equipment Manufacturers; Blaw-Knox Construction
Equipment Corporation (Mr David Wetjen); Grayston White
& Sparrow Ltd; Ingersoll-Rand Sales Company Ltd;
J C Bamford Excavators Ltd (Mr Tony Fellows); Liebherr
(Great Britain) Ltd; H. Leverton Ltd; Marubeni-Komatsu Ltd;
NCK Ltd; Perkins Engines.

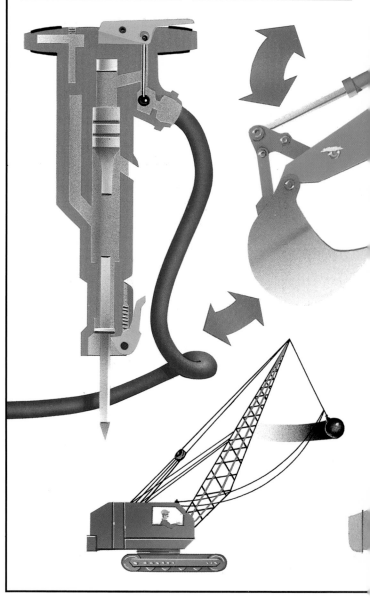

CONTENTS

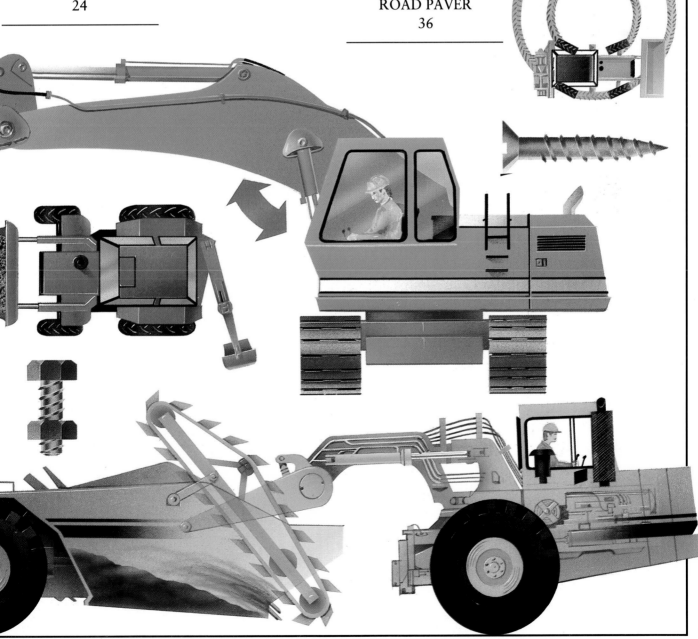

FAMOUS BUILDING FIRSTS

Fossils of stone tools have been found near the bones of *Homo habilis* ("handy man"), the earliest human species. *Homo habilis* lived in East Africa nearly 2 million years ago.

△ By 3000 B.C., the Egyptians were using copper saws. By 850 B.C., they were using iron saws to cut stone.

No one knows exactly when pulleys or cranes were invented, but the Assyrians are thought to have been using a simple rope and pulley system by about 1500 B.C.

△ In the 1st century B.C., the Roman architect and engineer Vitruvius published the first description of a crane, in his work *De architectura*. From Roman times on, cranes were often powered by human treadmills.

△ By A.D. 200, the wheelbarrow was being used in China. It wasn't known in Europe until the 1100s.

In the 1400s, the first metal screws and bolts appeared. Wood screws were first used around 1550, but the screwdriver wasn't invented until after the 1740s!

▽ In about 1480, the Italian artist and inventor Leonardo da Vinci designed the first pivoting (revolving) crane.

In 1796, a hydraulic ram using the pressure of water was invented by the Montgolfier brothers of France .

△ In 1818, French-born engineer Marc Isambard Brunel patented the first tunneling shield. It was used on a tunnel under the river Thames in London.

In 1859, the steam roller was invented by Louis Lemoine of France.

In 1861, the pneumatic drill was invented by the French engineer Germain Sommeiller, and used in constructing the Mont Cenis Tunnel through the Alps.

△ In 1895, the first electric hand drill was built by the German Wilhelm Fein. (Its forerunner, the awl, existed in prehistoric times.)

In 1904, in the U.S., Benjamin Holt invented crawler tracks. They were first used on a tractor in 1908.

In 1917, S. Duncan Black and Alonso G. Decker of the U.S. made the first electric drill with an on-off switch.

△ In the 1920s, truck-mounted cranes and cement mixers appeared. Bulldozers were developed at this time too, from crawler tractors.

In 1974, the Sears Tower was finished in Chicago. At 1,454 ft. (443 m), it is still the world's tallest building today.

INTRODUCTION

The great stone circles of Stonehenge, on Salisbury Plain in England, are a remarkable example of ancient building skills.

The earliest work on the site dates from about 2500 B.C. It was completed around 1500 B.C., when 80 huge stones, each weighing an average of 26 tons, were erected by levers and muscle power.

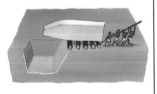

Archaeologists think that each stone was rolled to the edge of an oblong hole which had a sloping ramp on one side. The stone was levered into the hole and then pulled and levered upright.

The first person ever to use a stone ax to cut down a tree made as much use of a building machine as the driver of the biggest bulldozer in operation today. A machine is something that allows work to be done more easily or quickly, so the simple stone tools of prehistoric peoples were as useful to them as today's range of complex machinery is to us.

In some ways, modern building machines are not as complex as they may seem. As you will discover in this book, even the biggest is based on one of five simple machines — the lever, the wheel and axle, the pulley, the ramp, and the screw — and all these machines were invented thousands of years ago.

The most important change that has taken place over the centuries is in the way machines are powered. Until the invention of the steam engine in the 1700s, people had to rely on the power of their own muscles, or on animal, wind, or water power. It is amazing to think that all the great monuments of the past — the Egyptian pyramids, Roman bridges and aqueducts, the great medieval cathedrals — were built with only simple machines and muscle power!

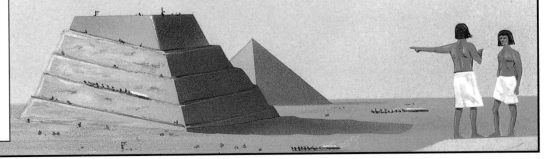

LEVERS – SHIFTING THE LOAD

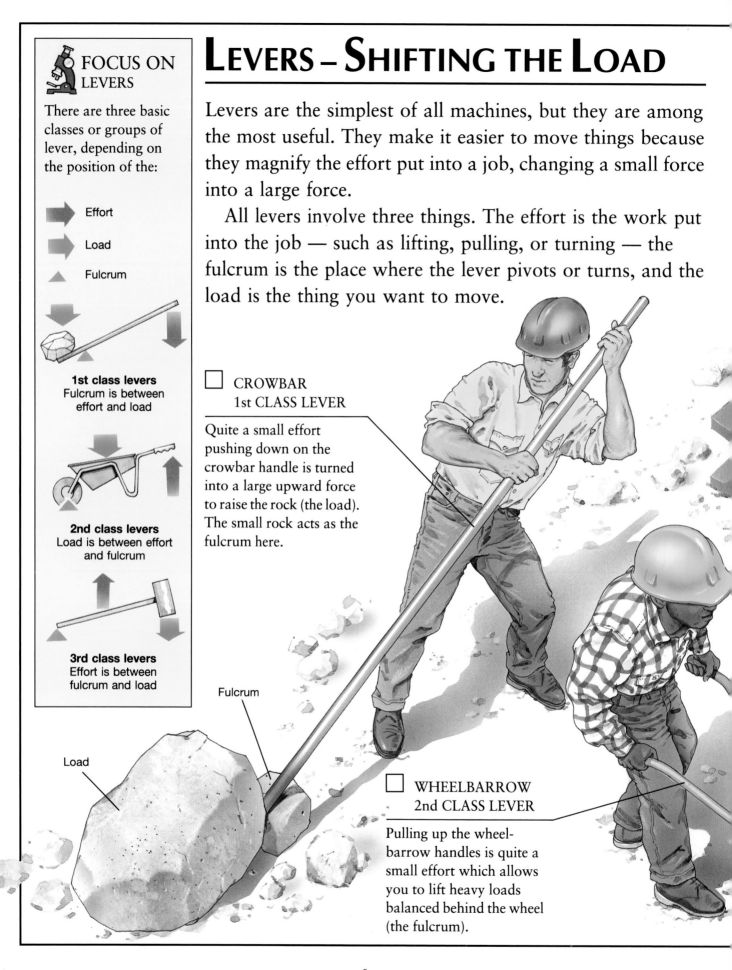

FOCUS ON LEVERS

There are three basic classes or groups of lever, depending on the position of the:

➡ Effort

➡ Load

▲ Fulcrum

1st class levers
Fulcrum is between effort and load

2nd class levers
Load is between effort and fulcrum

3rd class levers
Effort is between fulcrum and load

Levers are the simplest of all machines, but they are among the most useful. They make it easier to move things because they magnify the effort put into a job, changing a small force into a large force.

All levers involve three things. The effort is the work put into the job — such as lifting, pulling, or turning — the fulcrum is the place where the lever pivots or turns, and the load is the thing you want to move.

☐ CROWBAR
1st CLASS LEVER

Quite a small effort pushing down on the crowbar handle is turned into a large upward force to raise the rock (the load). The small rock acts as the fulcrum here.

Fulcrum

Load

☐ WHEELBARROW
2nd CLASS LEVER

Pulling up the wheel-barrow handles is quite a small effort which allows you to lift heavy loads balanced behind the wheel (the fulcrum).

The longer a lever is, and the closer the fulcrum is to the object, the easier it is to move the object. Test this out by resting a heavy book on the first inch of a 12-inch (30-cm) ruler. Slide a pencil (the fulcrum) under the ruler's 8-inch (20-cm) mark and use one finger to press down on the ruler end. Now move the pencil to the 4-inch (10-cm) mark and press down on the ruler again — it should be easier to raise the book now!

Fulcrum

☐ HAMMER 3rd CLASS LEVER

The hammer acts as a lever when it is used to hit the chisel down to break the rock. Here, the effort is lifting the hammer. The fulcrum is in the worker's shoulder joints, and the load is the hammer head.

☐ ALL SORTS OF LEVERS

There are hundreds of different levers. Many of the things you use every day are levers.

1st class lever
Spoon to lift lid

2nd class lever
Bottle opener

LEVERS IN ACTION

Excavators are machines that dig holes by scooping up and lifting out buckets of soil and rock. They are designed so that levers help them to do this heavy work. In size, excavators range from small machines that are used for ditch clearing, to large ones that can lift and dump as much as 20 tons of rock at one time. The depth of the hole the excavator digs depends on the length of the dipper arm and boom. The machine illustrated here can dig a hole over 16 feet (5 m) deep and lift a load weighing more than 1 ton.

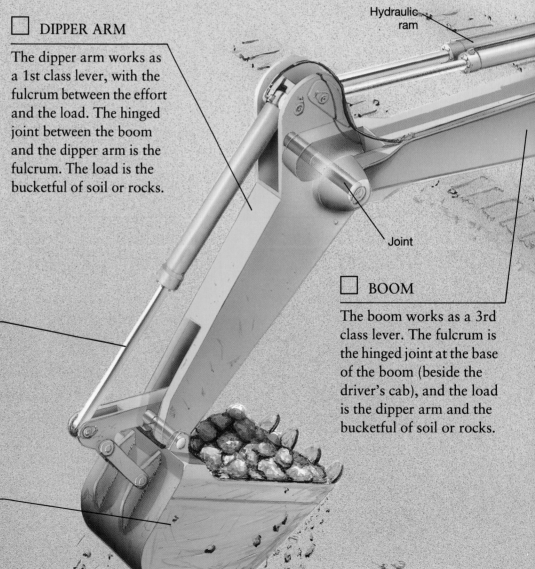

☐ DIPPER ARM

The dipper arm works as a 1st class lever, with the fulcrum between the effort and the load. The hinged joint between the boom and the dipper arm is the fulcrum. The load is the bucketful of soil or rocks.

Hydraulic ram

Joint

☐ HYDRAULIC RAMS

Hydraulic rams (see pages 10-11) slide in and out to make the boom, the dipper arm, and the bucket move.

☐ BOOM

The boom works as a 3rd class lever. The fulcrum is the hinged joint at the base of the boom (beside the driver's cab), and the load is the dipper arm and the bucketful of soil or rocks.

☐ BUCKET

The bucket is made of steel and has a toothed edge to help it bite into the ground.

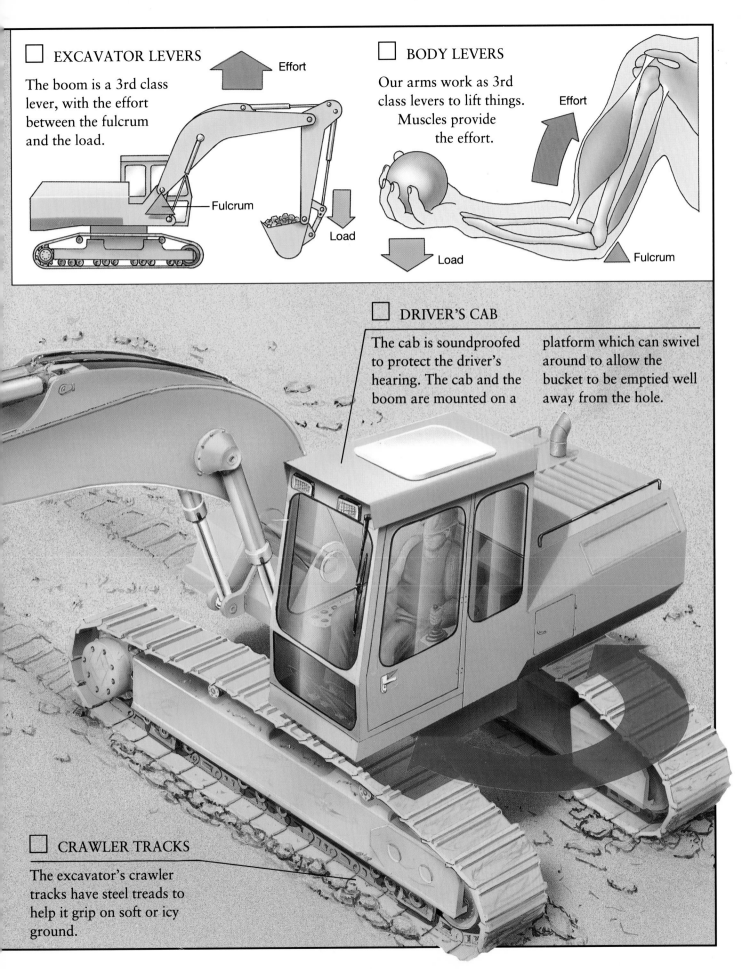

☐ EXCAVATOR LEVERS

The boom is a 3rd class lever, with the effort between the fulcrum and the load.

Effort

Fulcrum

Load

☐ BODY LEVERS

Our arms work as 3rd class levers to lift things. Muscles provide the effort.

Effort

Load

Fulcrum

☐ DRIVER'S CAB

The cab is soundproofed to protect the driver's hearing. The cab and the boom are mounted on a platform which can swivel around to allow the bucket to be emptied well away from the hole.

☐ CRAWLER TRACKS

The excavator's crawler tracks have steel treads to help it grip on soft or icy ground.

FOCUS ON COMPRESSION

One of the big differences between gases and liquids is that gases can be compressed (squeezed) into a smaller space, whereas liquids can't.

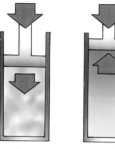

Gas   Liquid

Both liquids and gases can send a force through pipes, but liquids are usually used for the heavier tasks.

☐ HYDRAULIC FLUID

The hydraulic fluid used in building machines is a thin oil. Oil doesn't freeze in cold weather, and it keeps the moving parts working smoothly.

The moving parts of many building machines are operated hydraulically. Hydraulic systems use a liquid under pressure to send a force from one end of a pipe to another. If a pipe is connected to a cylinder with a piston inside it, and a liquid is pumped along the pipe into the cylinder, the liquid will push against the piston, forcing it to move. In an excavator, hydraulic fluid is used to push pistons that move the boom, dipper arm, and bucket.

☐ PISTON

The piston is a metal rod with a head that fits tightly inside the cylinder. As the piston slides up and down, it moves part of the building machine.

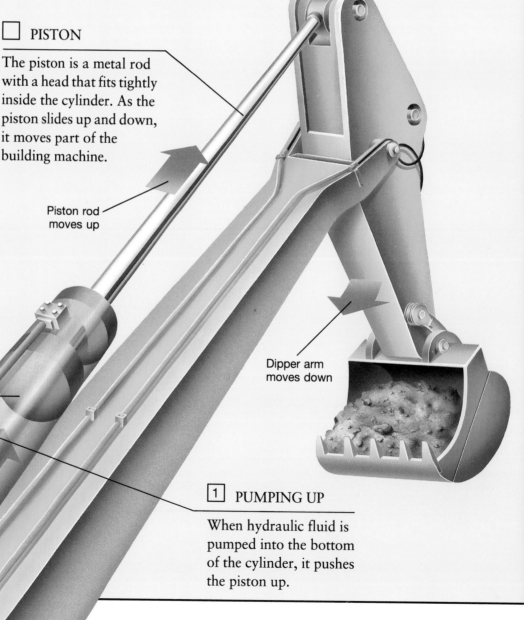

Piston rod moves up

Piston head

Dipper arm moves down

1 PUMPING UP

When hydraulic fluid is pumped into the bottom of the cylinder, it pushes the piston up.

Fill an icing syringe with water and push its nozzle into a length of tube. Push the syringe plunger right in, to fill the tube with water (ask a friend to hold the free end up over a sink.) Fill a second syringe with water, taking care not to pull air into the nozzle. Fix the nozzle to the other end of the tube, again trying not to let in any air.

Pushing one plunger in will now force the other one out, because the water sends a force (your push) along the piece of tube.

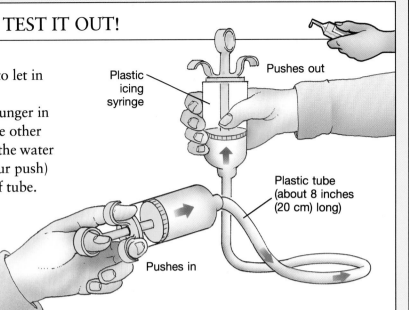

Plastic icing syringe

Pushes out

Plastic tube (about 8 inches (20 cm) long)

Pushes in

☐ PUMPING ALONG

Hydraulic fluid is pumped along pipes toward the cylinder. In most building machines, the pumps that push the fluid along are driven by the main engine.

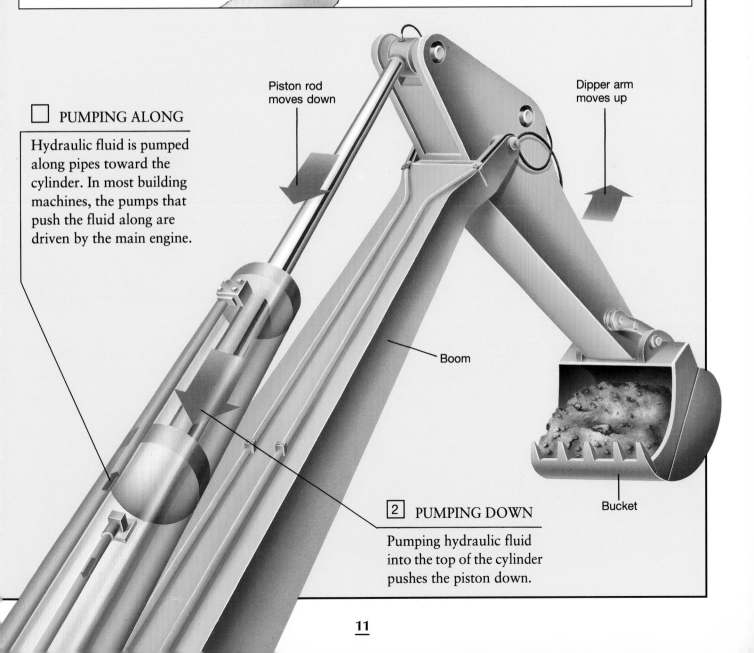

Piston rod moves down

Dipper arm moves up

Boom

Bucket

2 PUMPING DOWN

Pumping hydraulic fluid into the top of the cylinder pushes the piston down.

HYDRAULICS IN ACTION

In building machines, hydraulic systems are mainly used to move rams and jacks. A ram is a large cylinder and piston which acts rather like the muscles in an arm, pushing and moving parts of the machine about. Jacks are also large cylinders and pistons, but they work like legs and feet, helping to support and steady machines at work.

In most building machines, both the brakes and the steering operate hydraulically. Hydraulics are also used in aircraft — for example, to move the landing wheels in and out.

☐ BACKHOE LOADER

This machine has two hydraulically operated attachments, one at the front called the front loader, and one at the back called the backhoe.

☐ STABILIZERS

When the backhoe loader is used to do heavy work, hydraulic fluid is pumped along pipes to push out jacks called stabilizers.

These steady the machine and take the weight off the wheels and tires.

Front loader shovel

Backhoe bucket attachment

HYDRAULIC PIPES

Where they need to be able to move with parts of the machine, hydraulic pipes are made of flexible (bendy) material such as rubber. In other places, the pipes are made of metal.

HYDRAULIC RAM

When hydraulic fluid is pumped into the ram, it pushes a piston out. As the piston moves, it makes part of the backhoe move with it.

AT WORK

The backhoe loader is designed to do a wide variety of jobs. Besides digging trenches, these jobs include dozing (pushing soil and rocks out of the way) and grading (making rough ground level).

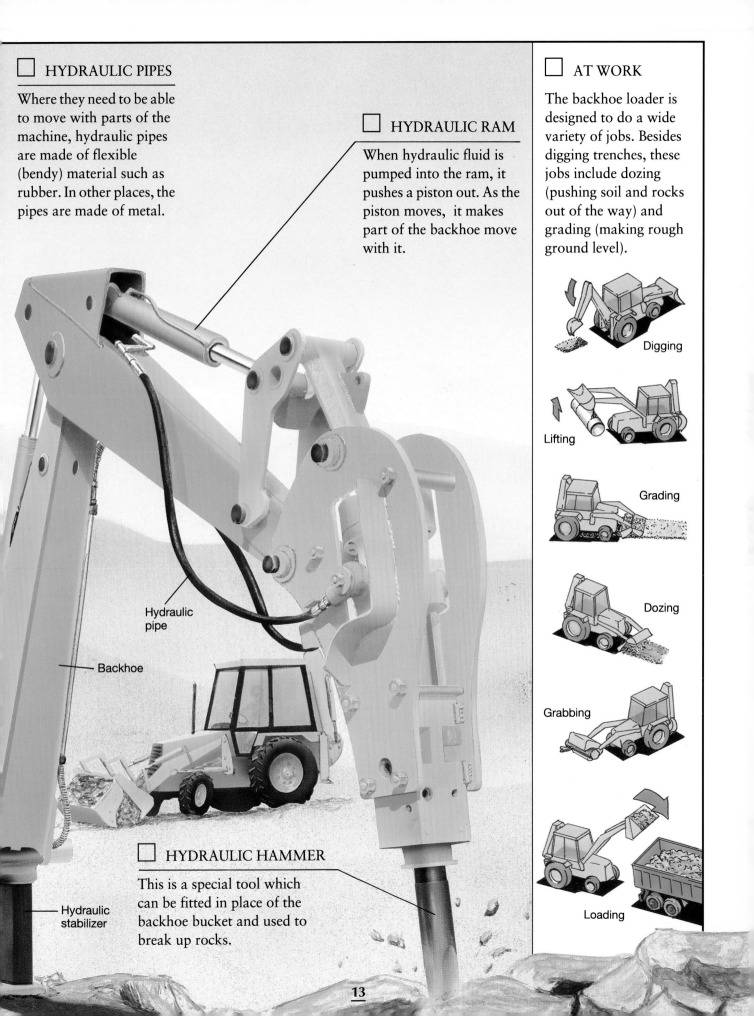

Digging

Lifting

Grading

Dozing

Grabbing

Loading

Hydraulic pipe

Backhoe

Hydraulic stabilizer

HYDRAULIC HAMMER

This is a special tool which can be fitted in place of the backhoe bucket and used to break up rocks.

FOCUS ON STEERING

Four-wheel steering (below) is not as common as two-wheel steering, but it gives vehicles far better turning and maneuvering ability.

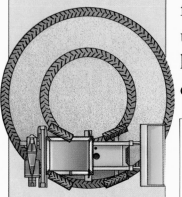

In vehicles with hydraulic steering, fluid is pumped into cylinders, to move pistons in and out. As the diagram below shows, these pistons move the wheels.

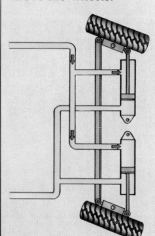

In many cars and trucks, the steering is controlled by a system of rods and gears, not by hydraulic systems.

AT THE CONTROLS

Most building machines have two different kinds of controls. They have driving controls, rather like those in a truck, and they have hydraulic controls to operate rams and jacks. The backhoe loader illustrated below (and on pages 12-13) has attachments front and back, so it has hydraulic controls front and back, as well as a steering wheel and all the other usual driving controls at the front. The backhoe loader's cab has glass all around, and the chair swivels to give the operator a good view whatever the direction of the job.

KEY TO BACKHOE LOADER CONTROLS

1 Steering wheel
2 Lever for horn, road and indicator lights, and to select forward or reverse driving.
3 Instrument panel — fuel gauge, oil and battery warning lights, etc.
4 Switch for selecting 2- or 4-wheel drive.
5 Windshield wiper switch
6 Gear lever
7 Transmission dump pedal (this works rather like the clutch in a car or a truck).
8 Brake pedals
9 Accelerator pedal
10 Hydraulic control lever for the front loader arm and shovel. Moving the lever back and forward raises and lowers the arms. Moving the lever left rolls the shovel back toward the driver. Moving it right tips the shovel forward to dump the load.
11 Hydraulic control lever for front loader attachments such as a clamshell bucket.
12 Cabin heating
13 Ignition (starter) switch
14 Parking brake
15 Remote boom lock — this holds the back-hoe safely against the machine when it is driven on roads.
16 Hydraulic control lever for the backhoe dipper arm and bucket
17 Hydraulic control levers for the stabilizer jacks
18 Hydraulic control for the backhoe boom

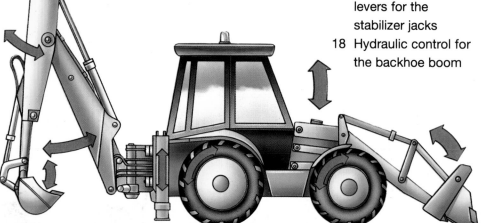

DUMPING THE LOAD

Wherever excavators and backhoe loaders are at work digging holes and trenches, there are great piles of rock and soil to clear away. This is a job for dump trucks, and on large construction sites there are usually fleets of them lining up to be filled. The trucks carry the building rubble to dump grounds. Twin hydraulic rams then push up each truck's body to dump the load.

☐ CANOPY

The canopy covers the driver's cab and the engine housing, protecting them from rock spills during loading and dumping.

TEST IT OUT!

Test how high a load has to be raised before it will slip to the ground. You will need something flat and smooth, like the back of a metal tray.

Take the tray outside and load it with a shovelful of soil. Now raise it slowly. How high do you have to lift it before it dumps its load?

☐ WHEELS AND TIRES

Dump trucks need giant wheels with heavy duty tires to provide good grip when hauling heavy loads over soft off-road surfaces.

☐ TRUCK BED

The sloping V-shaped floor of the bed helps to center the load and stop it shifting on hills.

☐ SMALL DUMPERS

Dump trucks come in all sizes. This one can carry about 1.5 tons — it's like a powered wheelbarrow.

☐ ENGINE POWER

Nearly all building machines are powered by diesel engines. These use diesel oil, a heavier fuel than the gasoline used in most cars. Two advantages of diesel engines are that they are more powerful than gasoline engines, and that diesel is cheaper than gasoline. The main difference between the two types of engine is in the way they ignite the fuel.

Diesel engine

☐ HYDRAULIC RAMS

A dump truck's twin hydraulic rams can raise the bed within seconds to dump a load. The giant dump truck shown here can carry a maximum load of nearly 90 tons.

JACKHAMMER AND COMPRESSOR

Compressors have many uses besides driving jackhammers. They produce high-pressure air to power spray-painters, sand-blasters for cleaning up the outside of buildings, and pile-drivers for hammering in bridge and building foundation piles. Compressors are also used to fill divers' tanks with air.

Air has enormous power, and very many uses, when it is put under pressure by compressing or squeezing it. When used to drive jackhammers, compressed air is strong enough to force a tool through rock or concrete!

Pneumatic or air-driven machines are safer than electrical equipment because they don't produce sparks that could start a fire or cause an explosion. There is also no danger from electric shocks, even when working in wet conditions.

☐ COMPRESSOR

There are three main types of compressor. In one, air is compressed by pistons moving up and down inside cylinders. In the others, air is forced past a spinning turbine or fan, or between two large rotating screws.

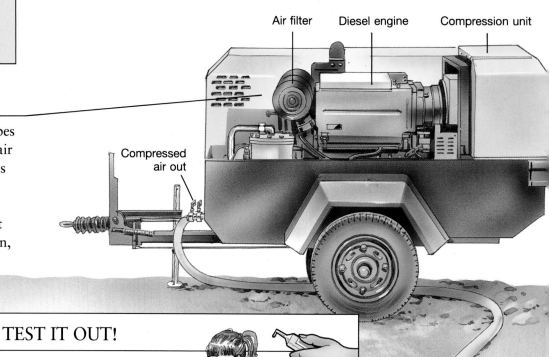

Air filter   Diesel engine   Compression unit

Compressed air out

Hose to jackhammer

TEST IT OUT!

Here's a way to see how powerful compressed air is. Take the nozzle off an empty dishwashing liquid bottle and press a small lump of modeling clay into the neck to make it airtight. (If you hold the bottle near your ear and squeeze gently you shouldn't hear any air escaping.)

Take the bottle out-side and lay it on the ground so that it isn't pointing toward anyone. Now jump on the bottle to squash it and compress the air inside. The modeling clay plug will shoot out at great speed, driven by the compressed air!

Plug shoots out

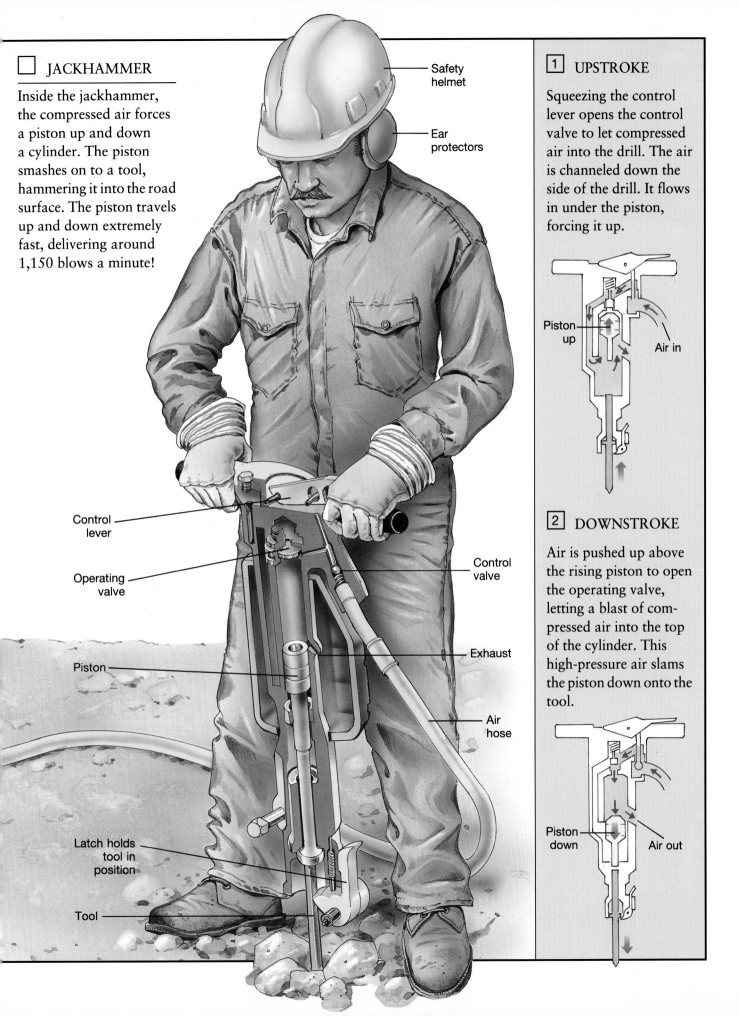

JACKHAMMER

Inside the jackhammer, the compressed air forces a piston up and down a cylinder. The piston smashes on to a tool, hammering it into the road surface. The piston travels up and down extremely fast, delivering around 1,150 blows a minute!

Safety helmet

Ear protectors

Control lever

Operating valve

Control valve

Exhaust

Air hose

Piston

Latch holds tool in position

Tool

1 UPSTROKE

Squeezing the control lever opens the control valve to let compressed air into the drill. The air is channeled down the side of the drill. It flows in under the piston, forcing it up.

Piston up

Air in

2 DOWNSTROKE

Air is pushed up above the rising piston to open the operating valve, letting a blast of compressed air into the top of the cylinder. This high-pressure air slams the piston down onto the tool.

Piston down

Air out

In scientific terms, work is said to be done when an object is moved by a force (a car is moved by a push, for example). The amount of work done is the size of the force multiplied by the distance the object moves. So the same amount of work can either move a heavy object a short distance or a lighter object a lot farther.

☐ REDUCING EFFORT

One person using a double pulley can lift the same weight as two people using a single one. The more pulleys you use, the less the effort needed.

Pulley Power

Like levers, pulleys are useful because they make it easier to lift things. A pulley is simply a grooved wheel around which a rope, chain, or cable is passed and tied to something heavy. The object is lifted by pulling down on the other end of the rope. One pulley can be used on its own, or several pulleys can be used together.

☐ SINGLE PULLEY

One pulley doesn't change the amount of effort in a job, but it does change the direction of the effort from a lift to a pull. And it's easier to pull a rope down than to lift something heavy up.

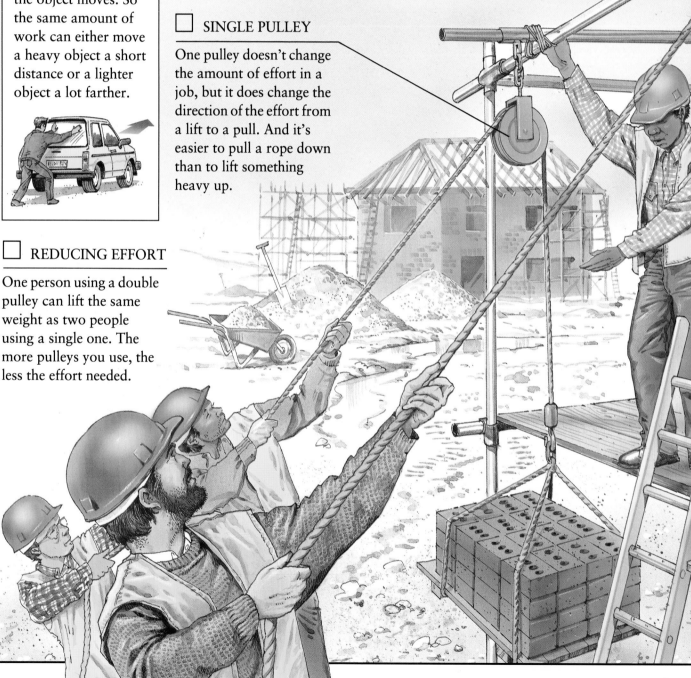

Pulley

Grooved rim stops tackle slipping out

Pulley

☐ DOUBLE PULLEY

Two pulleys cut the effort in half, but the rope must be pulled twice as far. More pulleys would cut the effort even further, but the rope would have to be pulled a greater distance.

☐ BLOCK AND TACKLE

Pulleys are mounted in frames called blocks. The rope, chain, or cable is called the tackle.

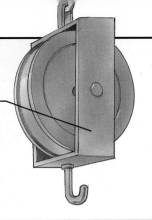

TEST IT OUT!

To make a single pulley, push some stiff wire through a thread spool and bend the ends round into a triangle. Hang the pulley from a hook. Tie one end of some string to a weight and loop the string over the pulley. How far do you have to pull the string to lift the weight 12 inches (30 cm)?

Unhook your single pulley and thread the string around it, so the wire hangs below the reel. Loop the rest of the string over the top spool.

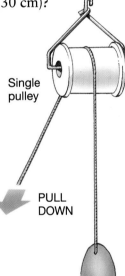

Single pulley

PULL DOWN

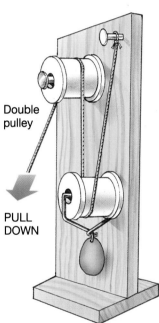

Double pulley

PULL DOWN

Now try a double pulley. Ask a grown-up to nail another spool to a piece of wood. Tie one end of the string to another nail alongside the spool.

Attach the same weight as before to the wire hook below the bottom spool. When you pull the string this time it should be easier to lift the weight. But how far do you now have to pull the string to lift the weight 12 inches (30 cm)?

A square frame is made much stronger when it is crossed diagonally by a brace or truss. You will often see braced squares in the framework of buildings, as well as in tower cranes.

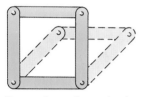

Square is easily pushed out of shape

Braced square is much stronger

TOWER CRANE

Cranes are machines that use pulleys to lift and move loads. Different types of crane are designed for different jobs, from loading containers full of goods onto ships, to moving heavy machinery around factories. The tallest cranes in the world are called tower cranes, and they are used to help construct skyscrapers and other tall structures where materials have to be raised to great heights.

☐ CRANE OPERATOR

The operator sits high above the building site in a cab reached by climbing up a ladder inside the framework of the tower.

Hoist cable

Trolley drum

Operator's cab

Hoist drum

☐ COUNTERWEIGHT

The crane's counterweight is made of heavy concrete blocks. It stops the load from pulling the crane over, by balancing the weight of the jib and the load being lifted.

☐ HOIST DRUM

This is driven by an electric motor. When it turns in one direction it winds the hoist cable in, when it turns the other way it lets the cable out.

Climbing frame

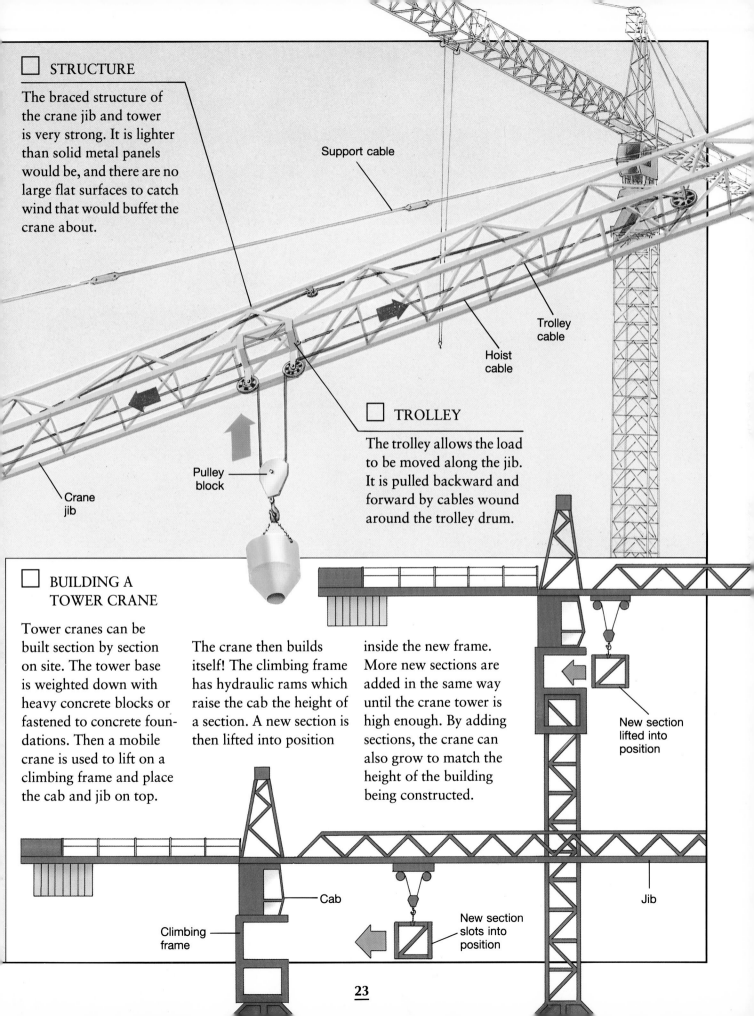

☐ STRUCTURE

The braced structure of the crane jib and tower is very strong. It is lighter than solid metal panels would be, and there are no large flat surfaces to catch wind that would buffet the crane about.

Support cable

Trolley cable

Hoist cable

Crane jib

Pulley block

☐ TROLLEY

The trolley allows the load to be moved along the jib. It is pulled backward and forward by cables wound around the trolley drum.

☐ BUILDING A TOWER CRANE

Tower cranes can be built section by section on site. The tower base is weighted down with heavy concrete blocks or fastened to concrete foundations. Then a mobile crane is used to lift on a climbing frame and place the cab and jib on top.

The crane then builds itself! The climbing frame has hydraulic rams which raise the cab the height of a section. A new section is then lifted into position

inside the new frame. More new sections are added in the same way until the crane tower is high enough. By adding sections, the crane can also grow to match the height of the building being constructed.

New section lifted into position

Jib

Cab

Climbing frame

New section slots into position

MOBILE CRANES

All objects behave as though their whole weight is concentrated in one place. This point is called the object's center of gravity or its balancing point. The lower an object's center of gravity, the more stable it is and therefore the harder it is to tip over.

Counterweights are used to adjust an object's center of gravity and to stop it toppling over.

Unlike tower cranes, mobile cranes are able to move about under their own power. There are different types. Dockside cranes are usually mounted on rails, for example, so they can travel up and down the length of the dock. Other cranes have crawler treads to spread their weight and help them grip on soft ground. Truck cranes have wheels and tires and can be driven along roads.

The biggest truck cranes are powerful enough to lift about 1,000 tons. Some have telescopic jibs that can extend to over 400 feet (130 m) above the ground. But the higher the jib extends, the less weight it can lift.

☐ OUTRIGGERS

Before it can start work, a truck crane has to put down stabilizer jacks to hold it steady and to take the weight off its wheels and tires. Hydraulic rams push out "arms" called outriggers. Then hydraulic jacks are lowered, raising the wheels off the ground.

☐ COUNTERWEIGHTS

Like tower cranes, truck cranes need counterweights to stop the objects they lift from pulling them over. The truck crane's counterweights are built in, at the base of the jib.

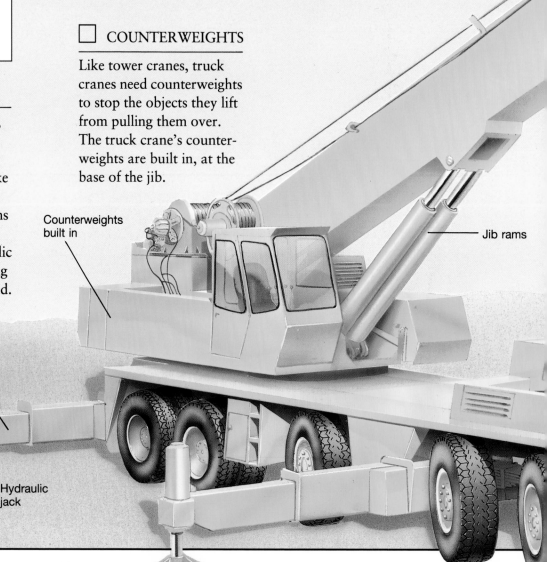

Counterweights
built in

Jib rams

Outrigger

Hydraulic
jack

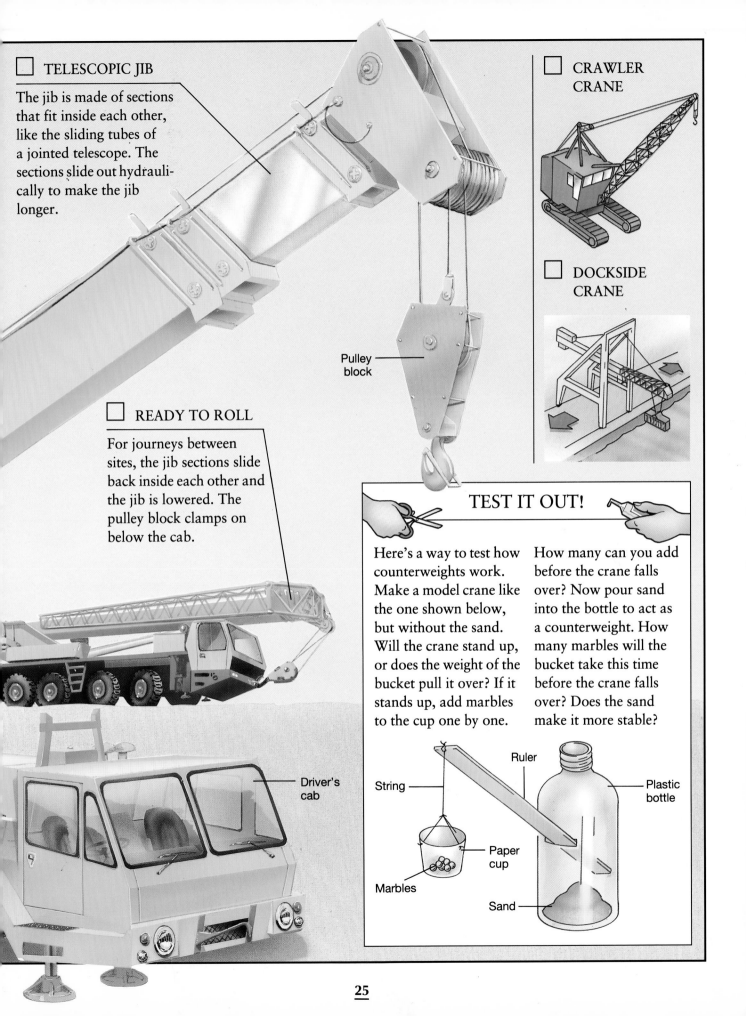

☐ TELESCOPIC JIB

The jib is made of sections that fit inside each other, like the sliding tubes of a jointed telescope. The sections slide out hydraulically to make the jib longer.

☐ CRAWLER CRANE

☐ DOCKSIDE CRANE

Pulley block

☐ READY TO ROLL

For journeys between sites, the jib sections slide back inside each other and the jib is lowered. The pulley block clamps on below the cab.

Driver's cab

TEST IT OUT!

Here's a way to test how counterweights work. Make a model crane like the one shown below, but without the sand. Will the crane stand up, or does the weight of the bucket pull it over? If it stands up, add marbles to the cup one by one.

How many can you add before the crane falls over? Now pour sand into the bottle to act as a counterweight. How many marbles will the bucket take this time before the crane falls over? Does the sand make it more stable?

String

Ruler

Plastic bottle

Paper cup

Marbles

Sand

WRECKING CRANE

Sometimes old buildings have to be knocked down and cleared away to make way for a road or a new building. Explosives may be used to blow the old building up, or machines may be used to knock it down. Sometimes the wrecking job is done by a mobile crane with a heavy weight attached to it. The weight is swung against the building or dropped down onto it — its smashing force is very effective whichever way it is used!

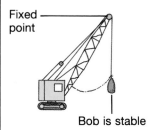

Fixed point

Bob is stable

If the bob is pushed or pulled to one side and then let go, it is pulled back in the opposite direction by the force of gravity.

Gravity makes bob swing

☐ FINE TIMING

One of the earliest uses for the pendulum was in clocks.

☐ CRAWLER CRANE

In the crane illustrated here, the jib can be derricked (raised or lowered) to alter its angle. The wrecking ball is attached to two cables. The hoist cable is used to lift and drop it, and the dragline to make it swing.

CRUNCH!

Some of the force of the ball's swing is absorbed as it crashes into the building. This stops the ball swinging back to smash into the crane cab!

Hoist cable

WRECKING BALL

The wrecking ball is made of hardened steel and may weigh several tons. It is pear shaped.

DRAGLINE CABLE

When the dragline cable is winched in, it pulls the wrecking ball with it. When the cable is released, the pendulum effect makes the ball swing toward the building.

FOCUS ON GALILEO

Galileo Galilei (1564-1642) was an Italian mathematics teacher and scientist. One of his discoveries was that the time it takes for a pendulum to complete one swing (known as its period) depends not on its weight, but on its length. Galileo is said to have made this discovery after watching the swing of a chandelier.

TEST IT OUT!

Here's a way to test Galileo's theory about the period of a pendulum. Tie a small weight and a big weight to two equal lengths of string.

Fasten each string to a hook and time ten swings. Both weights should take the same amount of time.

Now repeat the experiment, timing the same

weights first with a long piece of string, and then with a short one. You'll find the shorter pendulum swings faster than the long one!

Large weight

Small weight

Long string

Short string

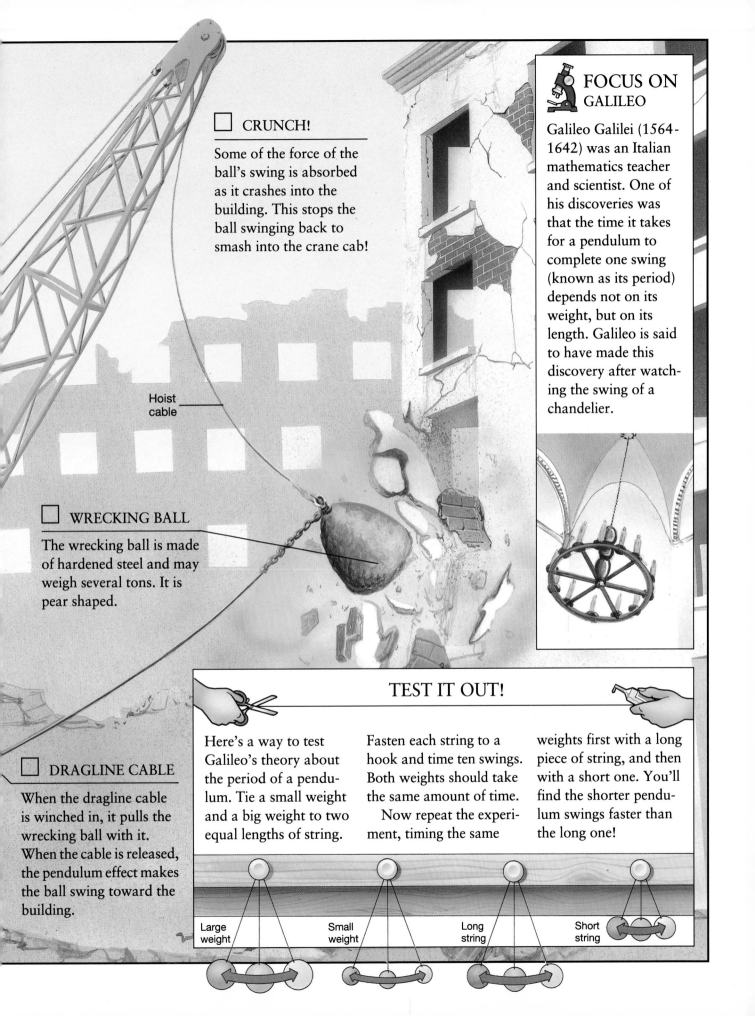

SCREWS AND SCREWDRIVERS

FOCUS ON TURNING

As a screwdriver turns, the force of the turn passes down to the screw head. This is smaller than the screwdriver handle, so it turns in a smaller circle. The difference in the turning circle increases the force of the turn. The screw pushes into the wood with greater force than that used to turn the screwdriver.

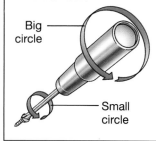

Big circle

Small circle

One of the easiest ways of moving a heavy weight is to pull or push it up a ramp, instead of trying to lift it straight up. So, because it makes work easier, a ramp is a simple machine. Surprisingly, screws have ramps in them — the thread of a screw is simply a ramp wrapped around a pole!

Screws have two main uses. One is for fixing and holding things together, and the other is for carrying a load.

☐ THREAD AND PITCH

The thread is the raised or ridged part of the screw. The pitch is the space between the turns of the thread. It is the distance the screw moves in one complete turn.

Screwdriver

☐ WOOD SCREW

Wood screws are used to fix and hold things together. As the screw is turned, its thread pulls it into the wood.

☐ NUT AND BOLT

The inside of the nut has a thread which matches that of the bolt. When the bolt is turned, it screws into the thread of the nut.

Wood screw

Wrench

Nut

Bolt

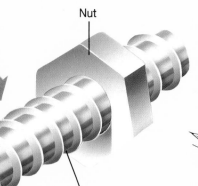

TEST IT OUT!

Here's a way to prove that the thread of a screw is like a ramp. Cut a piece of paper into a ramp shape and wrap it tightly around a pencil. The sloping edge of the paper will spiral around the pencil, just like the thread of a screw.

Paper

Pencil

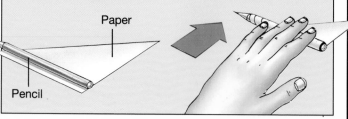

CONSTRUCTION AUGER

An auger is a screw with a wide deep thread that can be used to carry a load — for example, lifting soil up out of a hole. A construction auger is used to drill holes to take pipes or foundation piles, so its thread often has a sharp edge to help it cut into the ground.

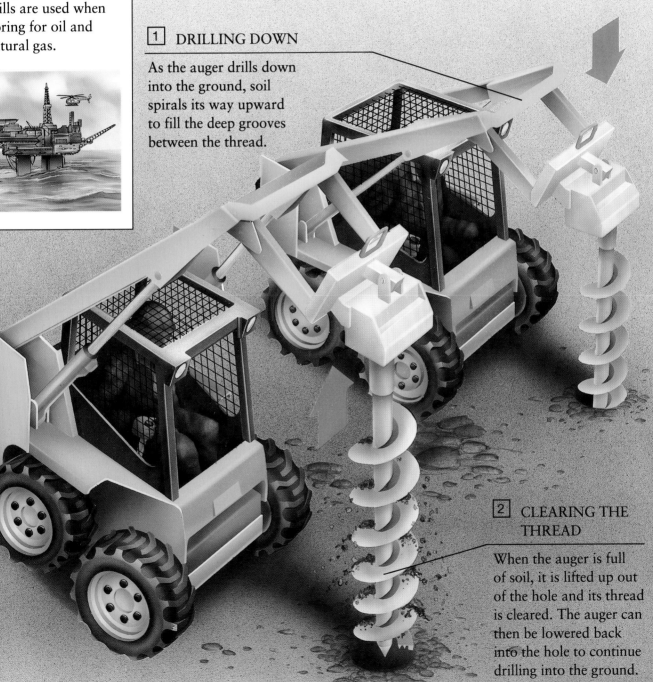

1 DRILLING DOWN

As the auger drills down into the ground, soil spirals its way upward to fill the deep grooves between the thread.

2 CLEARING THE THREAD

When the auger is full of soil, it is lifted up out of the hole and its thread is cleared. The auger can then be lowered back into the hole to continue drilling into the ground.

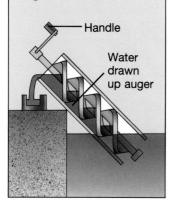
CEMENT MIXER

The drum of a cement mixer does two things. When it turns in one direction it mixes the concrete inside it. When it turns in the other direction it works like a device known as an Archimedes screw, to raise the concrete to the mouth of the drum so that it pours down the delivery chute.

Transit truck mixers deliver ready-mixed concrete to building sites. Materials for making concrete are poured into the drum before the truck starts off. Then, as the truck drives along, its drum turns to keep the concrete moving.

☐ ENGINE POWER

Like most trucks, transit truck mixers are powered by diesel engines. The drum is driven either by the main engine or by a separate engine, mounted below the water tank.

TEST IT OUT!

Ask a grown-up to cut the top and bottom off a plastic bottle and help you to wrap and tape about 5 feet (1.5 m) of clear plastic tubing tightly around it. Now hold your Archimedes screw in a bowl of water and turn it very quickly. Water will be drawn up the tube!

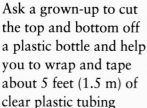

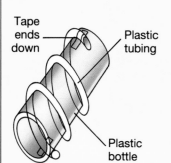

Tape ends down

Plastic tubing

Plastic bottle

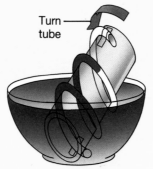

Turn tube

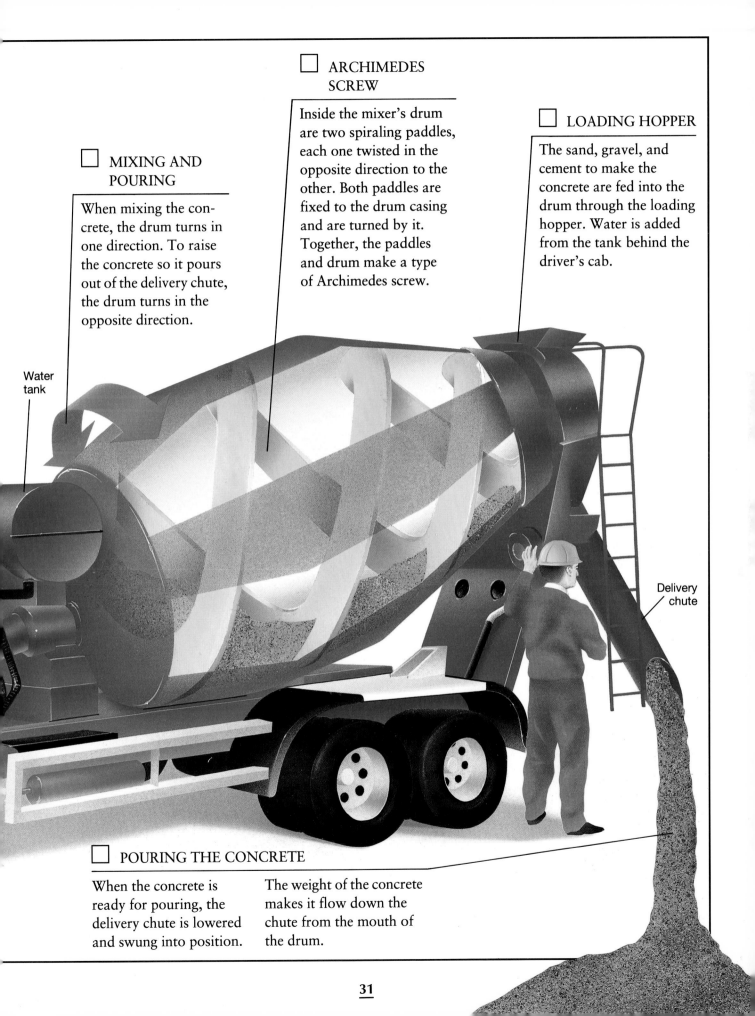

☐ ARCHIMEDES
SCREW

Inside the mixer's drum are two spiraling paddles, each one twisted in the opposite direction to the other. Both paddles are fixed to the drum casing and are turned by it. Together, the paddles and drum make a type of Archimedes screw.

☐ LOADING HOPPER

The sand, gravel, and cement to make the concrete are fed into the drum through the loading hopper. Water is added from the tank behind the driver's cab.

☐ MIXING AND
POURING

When mixing the concrete, the drum turns in one direction. To raise the concrete so it pours out of the delivery chute, the drum turns in the opposite direction.

Water
tank

Delivery
chute

☐ POURING THE CONCRETE

When the concrete is ready for pouring, the delivery chute is lowered and swung into position.

The weight of the concrete makes it flow down the chute from the mouth of the drum.

FOCUS ON STRUCTURE

Tunnel walls are curved or arched because a circle is a much stronger shape than a square (unless the square is braced, and you can't brace a tunnel). You can prove this if you make two tunnels — a round one and a square one — from two rectangular pieces of stiff cardboard.

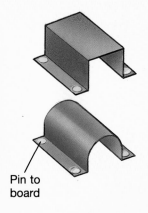

Pin to board

Place coins of the same size on each tunnel, one at a time. The weakest tunnel will collapse first.

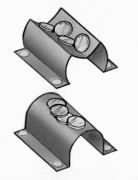

TUNNEL-BORING MACHINE

Tunnel-boring machines (TBMs for short) are used to build large tunnels to carry roads and railroads through mountains and under cities, rivers, and even the sea. They work rather like giant drills, boring their way through the ground. But they can only cut into rocks that are soft and firm, such as chalk, clay, or soft sandstone.

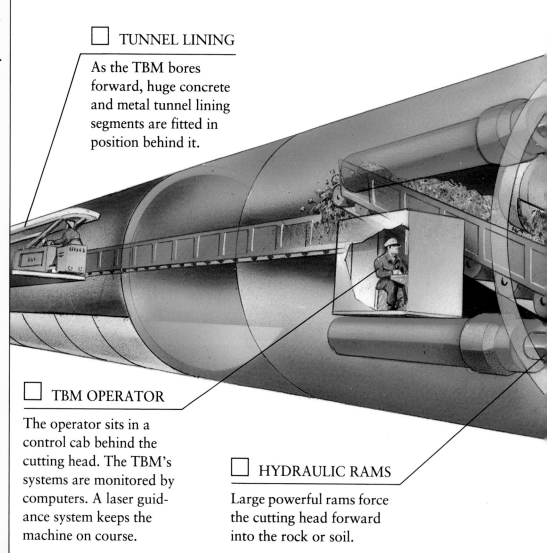

☐ TUNNEL LINING

As the TBM bores forward, huge concrete and metal tunnel lining segments are fitted in position behind it.

☐ TBM OPERATOR

The operator sits in a control cab behind the cutting head. The TBM's systems are monitored by computers. A laser guidance system keeps the machine on course.

☐ HYDRAULIC RAMS

Large powerful rams force the cutting head forward into the rock or soil.

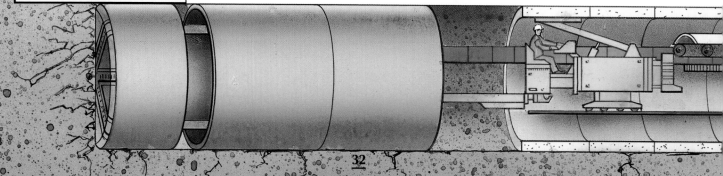

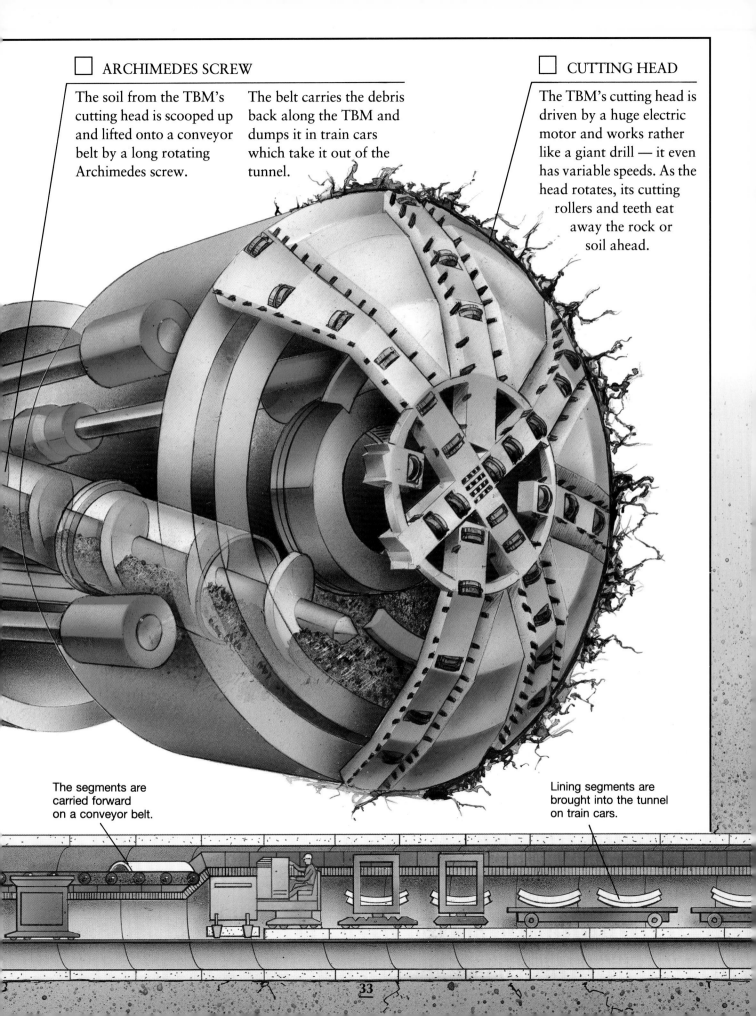

☐ ARCHIMEDES SCREW

The soil from the TBM's cutting head is scooped up and lifted onto a conveyor belt by a long rotating Archimedes screw.

The belt carries the debris back along the TBM and dumps it in train cars which take it out of the tunnel.

☐ CUTTING HEAD

The TBM's cutting head is driven by a huge electric motor and works rather like a giant drill — it even has variable speeds. As the head rotates, its cutting rollers and teeth eat away the rock or soil ahead.

The segments are carried forward on a conveyor belt.

Lining segments are brought into the tunnel on train cars.

FOCUS ON WEIGHT

Bulldozers rarely get bogged in mud even though they are very heavy (the one shown opposite weighs over 11.5 tons). This is because they exert (put out) less pressure on the ground than a full-grown person does. A bulldozer's weight is spread over its long wide crawler tracks, but a person's weight is concentrated on two small feet.

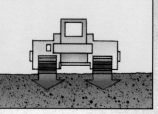

PUSHING AND SHOVING

Some of the heaviest construction jobs are done by machines that push and shove. Using strong steel blades they clear sites of rock and soil. Then they shape and level rough ground to take the foundations of bridges, buildings, or roads.

Bulldozers start the ground-preparing work for new roads. Scrapers have a knifelike cutting blade which levels ground by slicing off a layer of soil.

☐ SCRAPER

As the scraper moves forward, its blade slices off a layer of earth and rubble. This is pushed into the bowl by the elevator flights, as they swing past the blade, moving round like escalator stairs.

Elevator flights

Scraper blade

☐ SCRAPER BOWL

The trailer part of the scraper is called the bowl. It's made of tough steel and can hold a load of more than 17 tons.

☐ BULLDOZER

This word was first used in the 1870s. At the time it meant any kind of hard punishment, as in "a dose fit for a bull". It has come to be used for machines since the 1920s. Small machines are sometimes called calfdozers.

☐ SHOVING SNOW

Snowplows keep roads clear of snow. Their blades vary. Single blades are set at an angle so the snow is pushed to one side of the road.

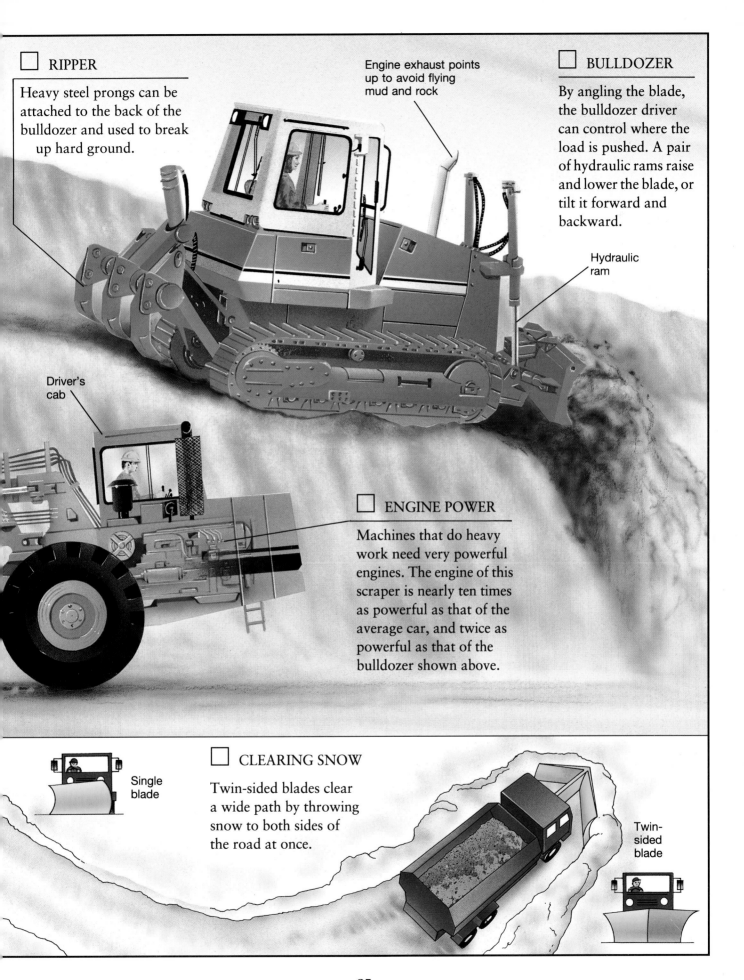

☐ RIPPER

Heavy steel prongs can be attached to the back of the bulldozer and used to break up hard ground.

Engine exhaust points up to avoid flying mud and rock

☐ BULLDOZER

By angling the blade, the bulldozer driver can control where the load is pushed. A pair of hydraulic rams raise and lower the blade, or tilt it forward and backward.

Hydraulic ram

Driver's cab

☐ ENGINE POWER

Machines that do heavy work need very powerful engines. The engine of this scraper is nearly ten times as powerful as that of the average car, and twice as powerful as that of the bulldozer shown above.

Single blade

☐ CLEARING SNOW

Twin-sided blades clear a wide path by throwing snow to both sides of the road at once.

Twin-sided blade

FOCUS ON ASPHALT

Asphalt is made from bitumen (a sticky dark liquid obtained from crude oil during petroleum refining), mixed with crushed limestone and sand. Sometimes asphalt is found naturally — there is an asphalt lake in the West Indies called Trinidad Lake.

West Indies

South America

ROAD PAVER

Modern roads are made safe and strong by sandwiching layers of different materials together. Most of the layers are put down by machines called road pavers. These are specially designed to lay an even ribbon of road, with none of the bumps that would be a nightmare for fast traffic.

Road paving is a slow and careful job, particularly when laying the surface layers of asphalt. During this stage the road paver crawls along very slowly.

4 SCREED

The asphalt is flattened and smoothed by a heavy attachment called the screed, which fits on to the paver behind the auger. The up-and-down action of tampers and vibrators inside the screed helps to press down the asphalt, but the finishing is mainly done by the soleplate and the weight of the screed.

5 SOLEPLATE

This works rather like a hot iron, to flatten and smooth the asphalt. It is beneath the screed, heated by burners inside it.

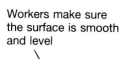

Workers make sure the surface is smooth and level

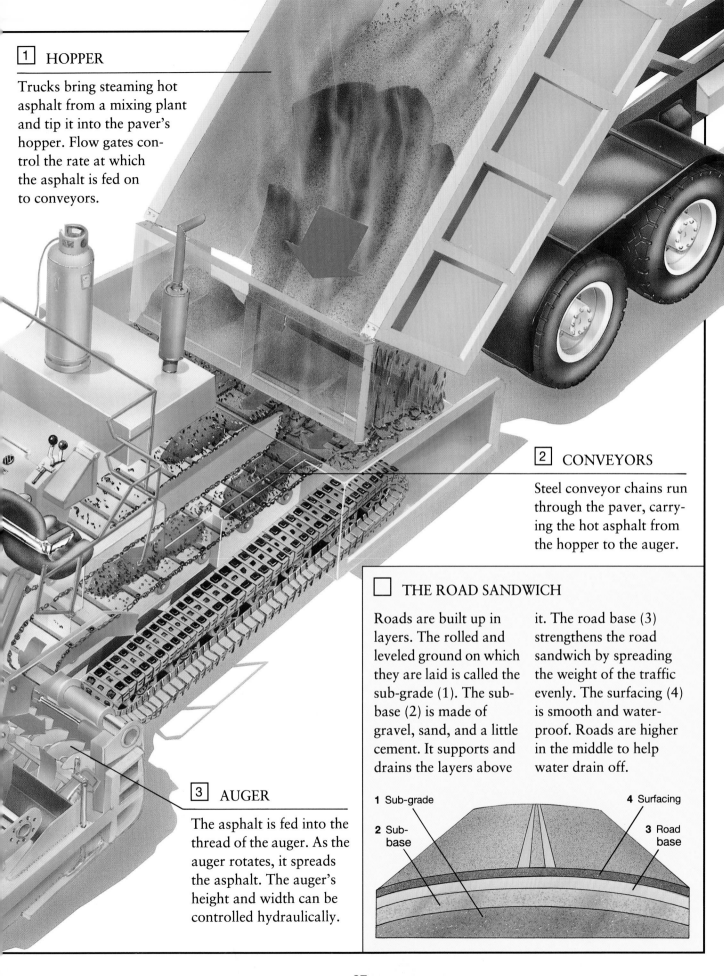

1 HOPPER

Trucks bring steaming hot asphalt from a mixing plant and tip it into the paver's hopper. Flow gates control the rate at which the asphalt is fed on to conveyors.

2 CONVEYORS

Steel conveyor chains run through the paver, carrying the hot asphalt from the hopper to the auger.

THE ROAD SANDWICH

Roads are built up in layers. The rolled and leveled ground on which they are laid is called the sub-grade (1). The sub-base (2) is made of gravel, sand, and a little cement. It supports and drains the layers above it. The road base (3) strengthens the road sandwich by spreading the weight of the traffic evenly. The surfacing (4) is smooth and waterproof. Roads are higher in the middle to help water drain off.

1 Sub-grade

2 Sub-base

4 Surfacing

3 Road base

3 AUGER

The asphalt is fed into the thread of the auger. As the auger rotates, it spreads the asphalt. The auger's height and width can be controlled hydraulically.

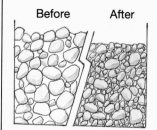
The weight of a steam-roller can smooth a bed of gravel or sand, but vibrations pack it really solid. Vibrations are very fast up and down movements. They get rid of the air pockets that weaken a road, by making sand and gravel jump about until they settle into every available space. This makes the road much more compact and strong.

Before   After

ROLLING AND PACKING

If a road isn't strongly built it will soon begin to break up under the pounding of the thousands of cars and trucks that drive along it. To make a road strong and firm, each of its layers must be flattened until it is hard and smooth. Rolling and packing machines use weight and vibration to do this important job.

☐ RAMMER

The "foot" of this hand-held machine vibrates, moving rapidly up and down to flatten narrow strips of sand, gravel, or asphalt. Its packing force is 2,000 pounds (900 kg), which is more than ten times its own weight (when still).

☐ ROLLERS

Grass rollers work in exactly the same way as steamrollers. They flatten ground to give a smooth surface for lawn tennis courts.

☐ SINGLE ROLLER

Rollers come in different sizes, to suit different jobs. This small roller is useful when laying sidewalks or repairing roads. Its drum vibrates as it rolls.

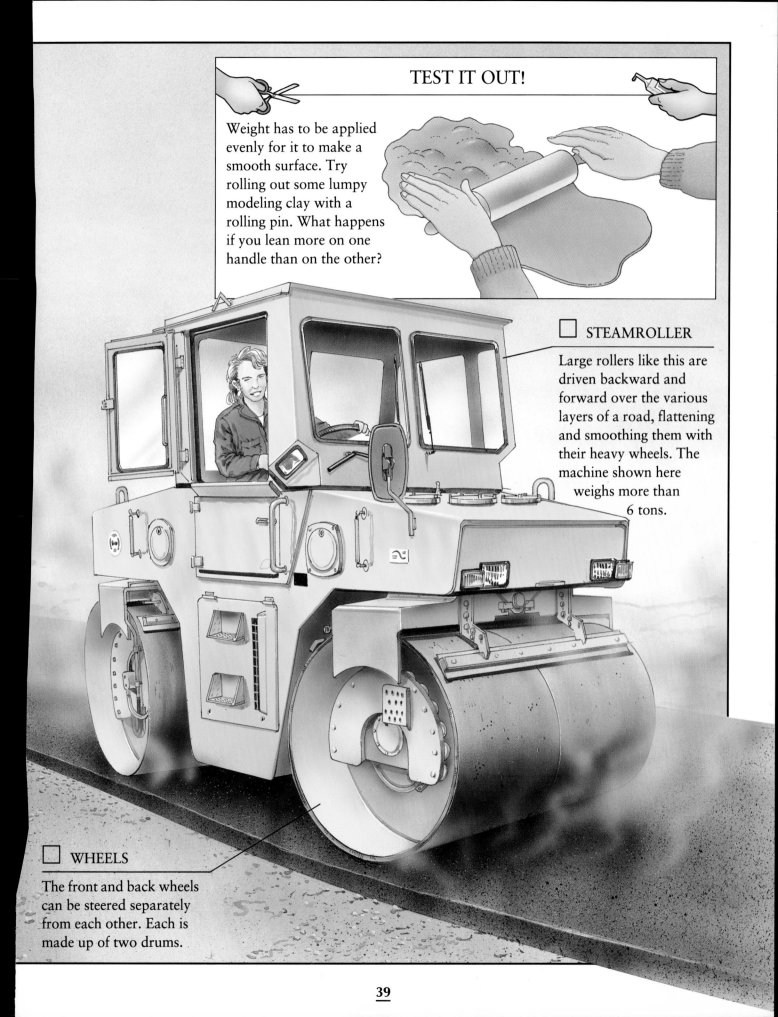

TEST IT OUT!

Weight has to be applied evenly for it to make a smooth surface. Try rolling out some lumpy modeling clay with a rolling pin. What happens if you lean more on one handle than on the other?

☐ STEAMROLLER

Large rollers like this are driven backward and forward over the various layers of a road, flattening and smoothing them with their heavy wheels. The machine shown here weighs more than 6 tons.

☐ WHEELS

The front and back wheels can be steered separately from each other. Each is made up of two drums.

INDEX

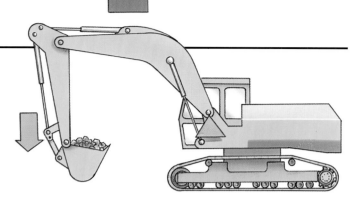

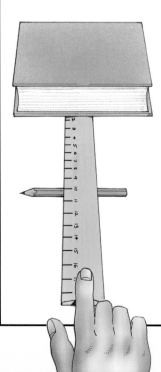